REDSKIN MORNING

REDSKIN MORNING

And Other Stories

BY

JOAN GRANT

ILLUSTRATED BY
RALPH LAVERS

METHUEN & CO. LTD. LONDON
36 Essex Street Strand W.C.2

FOR
COLIN

First published in 1944

BOOK
PRODUCTION
WAR ECONOMY
STANDARD

THIS BOOK IS PRODUCED IN
COMPLETE CONFORMITY WITH THE
AUTHORIZED ECONOMY STANDARDS

PRINTED IN GREAT BRITAIN

CONTENTS

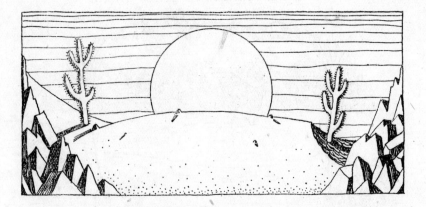

REDSKIN MORNING

THE Lord of Earth was young, as age is judged among the
Gods, and after he had made mountains and valleys, forests
and fish, birds to people his sky and many kinds of animals,
he found himself longing for some one with whom to talk of
all that he had done . . . for even a god is lonely without
a companion.

He worked so swiftly that he could make a range of hills
between sunrise and sunset, and turn a desert into a place of
many waters between noon and the time of lengthening
shadows : yet he spent seven days and seven nights before
he was ready to speak the words which gave life to his son.
Then, like an echo to the Words, he heard his son say to him :

' You must be a great magician, Father. For now I am, and
a moment ago I was not. I was nowhere, and now I am here.'

And the Lord of Earth called his son ' Ka-ru-in ', ' Son of
the Morning '.

Together they walked through meadows which the Father
had made out of barren plains, and climbed mountains he had
made out of nothing. And one day Ka-ru-in said :

' Will you teach me to make things like you do ? '

The Lord of Earth hesitated before answering : he knew
that he could not tell his son how to give life, for that is the
secret of the Gods, yet he loved his son so dearly that he could
not bear to refuse him anything.

'Together we can make things. You must draw what you wish to be brought alive, and then show me your pictures, so that I can tell you whether they would be comfortable bodies for life to live in.'

So Ka-ru-in went down to the river, and with a stick he drew a fish in the soft mud of the bank . . . a fish as long as a canoe and with an eye larger than a cooking-pot. Then he ran to his father, crying out, 'Come quickly, for the fish I have made is ready to learn to swim.'

The Father looked at the drawing, and then he said, 'Are you sure there is nothing about this fish you would like to alter?'

'Nothing,' said Ka-ru-in. 'It is a beautiful fish, and I am sure it could not be better.'

'Isn't it too big?'

'I want it big,' said Ka-ru-in firmly. '*Any one* can make a *little* fish.'

'Nothing could hide from such enormous eyes, and it is so large that it would never be content to feed only on water-weed. It might feel so hungry that it ate my fish . . . and after hundreds of them it would still be unsatisfied.'

'I hadn't thought of that,' said Ka-ru-in. 'Perhaps I had better draw another one for you.'

And he picked up the pointed stick and drew a fish that was no larger than the palm of his hand.

'That is much better,' said the Father; 'but you must give it some gills or it won't be able to breathe.'

So Ka-ru-in drew another line to show where the gills were to be, and his Father said:

'Perhaps its tail might be a little wider, otherwise it will not be able to swim fast enough to amuse itself.'

So Ka-ru-in made more lines for the tail, and his Father said proudly, 'Now indeed it is a beautiful fish! Shut your eyes for a moment, and when you open them you have only to wade into the river to see your fish come swimming towards you.'

Then the Lord of Earth knelt down and pressed his forehead against the mud where the fish was drawn, and he whispered to it . . . but no one who is not ready to become the Lord of an Earth will ever know what he whispered. From the river sounded a splash, as the new fish entered the water for the first time. When Ka-ru-in saw his fish he was so excited that he shouted for joy.

The next day he decided to make an animal which he could take about with him, so he would not have to go down to the river whenever he wanted to admire his cleverness. He made it long and thin, and covered it with scales . . . for he had found while drawing the fish that scales are easy to make with a pointed stick. Then he called his Father to come to see what he had done, saying: 'It is a land animal, which is why I haven't given it anything to swim with and why it doesn't need gills.'

'Haven't you forgotten something? You haven't given it any legs.'

Ka-ru-in *had* forgotten the legs, but he wasn't going to admit it, so he said: '*Any one* can make an animal with legs, but my special animal doesn't need them.'

'But if it hasn't legs, or wings, and it can't swim, how is it going to move about?'

'Like this,' said Ka-ru-in, flinging himself flat on the ground and squirming along on his belly. Then, as he found he didn't get along very fast, he added: 'You are so very clever at making things work, that surely you won't spoil my lovely new animal just because you never thought of making one without legs ? '

' I will try . . . if you will cover your ears with your hands and shut your eyes. . . .'

The Lord of Earth plucked a flash of lightning from a cloud and laid it on the legless animal to give it swiftness : then he whispered to it, the Words which must never be heard by mortals.

' Open your eyes, Ka-ru-in,' he said urgently, ' or it will have disappeared before you see it . . . for even I never expected it to move so fast ! '

All that Ka-ru-in saw of the first snake was the tip of its tail as it slid into a hole under a boulder.

The next day he couldn't think of anything interesting to draw, so he sat on the river bank, poking his stick into the mud, until he decided to practise diving in the deep pool where the river widened.

The Father found the shallow holes made by the stick, and thought they were Ka-ru-in's idea for a new animal, so he added a line to each of them and turned them into tadpoles. When he saw that his son was disappointed with tadpoles, he turned them into frogs, which hopped about, croaking at each other, and made Ka-ru-in laugh. He loved hearing his son laugh, so he decided that tadpoles should always turn into frogs . . . which is why they do so even to this day.

Ka-ru-in was very disappointed in his snake, for it moved so fast that he never saw it except as a streak in the distance ; so he decided not to make any more things until he had learned to be even better at drawing. The impressions in the soft mud were spoiled whenever it rained, so he found a cave on whose smooth walls he could make enduring pictures that need not be finished in a hurry. Sometimes he would spend three days deciding what kind of tail his new animal should have, or three moons to consider the curve of a shoulder. It took him nearly a year before he was satisfied with a drawing, and even while it was only lines on rock he could almost hear the surge of its hooves and see the great head tossing in its pride.

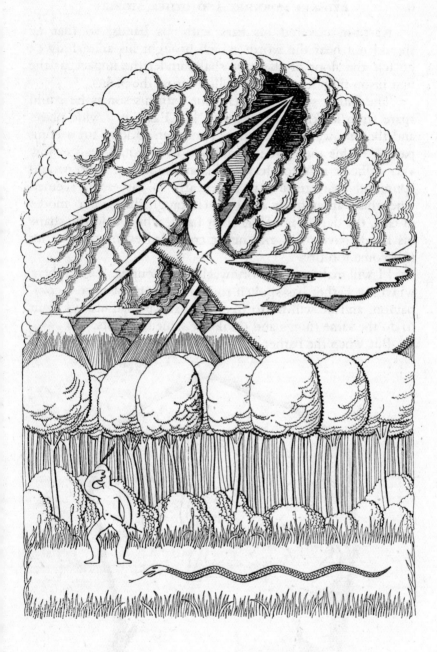

Ka-ru-in covered his ears with his hands, so that he should not hear the words which brought his animal alive : he felt the floor of the cave shake under the impact, as the first bison thundered out to gallop across the plains.

The Father spent as much time with his son as he could spare from looking after Earth : but Earth is a wide place, and the boy was often alone. He began to long for a companion of his own age ; some one who would realize how very difficult it is to draw a bison, some one who would appreciate that creation is not nearly so easy as it seemed when his Father made things. He taught himself to model in clay, the dark clay of the river bank, which held the shape his hands gave to it, and never crumbled even when he let it become too dry.

' I will make a model of myself,' he thought. ' And then, when my Father has spoken to it, I shall at last have a companion, and he will be so like me that we shall always want to do the same things and think the same thoughts.'

But when the Father saw the model made in the image of

his son, he said reluctantly, ' For the first time I must refuse to do what you ask of me. It took me seven days and seven nights to create you, my son, and every part of that creation had to be done by me, alone.'

When the Father saw the disappointment of Ka-ru-in, he said gently, 'Do you long for a companion even as I longed for you ? '

' Yes,' said Ka-ru-in, ' and I shall never be happy until he is with me.'

' Then I will make him for you ; but it will take me seven moons ; for he must be as wise as you now are, which is far wiser than you were when you first became.'

To Ka-ru-in, who had been looking forward so eagerly to having a companion before sunset, seven moons seemed as slow as eternity. 'I don't want *you* to make him,' he said passionately. ' I want *this* boy to come alive, this boy whom *I* have created ! '

' I cannot do that,' said the Father sadly.

' You mean you *won't* do it ! You are jealous because I have become so skilled in making things. You want to be the only one who can make a man, so that you can always feel older and wiser and more important than I am ! '

Then Ka-ru-in wept with rage and disappointment, and ran away, leaving the Father looking sorrowfully after him.

Ka-ru-in knew he must never listen to the secret words, but now the temptation to hear them echoed his footsteps. ' You are his son, Ka-ru-in,' said the voice of temptation. ' The secret is your heritage. He is withholding from you that which is yours by right. Why do you not follow him into the forest, and listen ? You have often seen him hold up his hands to the sky : then his lips move, and a new kind of bird alights on the tree above him, or a butterfly of a colour never before seen sways on a flower among the meadow grasses. Watch him Ka-ru-in ; listen to him, and then you need no longer *ask* for his help.'

For a time Ka-ru-in tried to forget the voice of temptation, which came out of the mouth of the first snake. But it was

2

only easy to forget when he was beside the river, for there the rippling water seemed to whisper to him, 'Don't listen to the snake, Ka-ru-in.' It was not the river but the little fish he had made which spoke to him, but he did not recognize it.

He was alone on the plains when he decided to use *any* means to wrest the secret from his Father. A herd of bison, his *own* bison, had galloped past him, dark as a thunder cloud, proud as a storm.

'You are *my* bison' he cried out. 'I, Ka-ru-in, made you. I am too great to acknowledge any one my master!'

And the pride of Ka-ru-in spoke louder than the little fish, louder even than the snake : so when the Lord of Earth went into the forest, his son followed him, hiding in the deep shadows, sliding quiet as the snake from tree to tree.

The Father knew that he had been betrayed, for the white dove he tried to create appeared as a black raven, and instead of flying up into the sunlight, it flapped disconsolate wings and with dismal croakings hid itself in a dark thicket.

And Ka-ru-in had heard the secret words : and he ran to where he had hidden the image of himself, the image made from the dark clay of the river bank. He kissed it on the forehead, and on the breast, and on the feet : then he whispered to it the Words which mortals must never hear. And the image was no longer of clay : it had become a youth, lying asleep on the floor of the cave.

He sat up, opened his eyes, and said, 'Indeed you are a great magician : for I am, and I was not. I was nowhere, and now I am here.'

Then was Ka-ru-in well content, for surely he was the equal of the Lord of Earth ? And he called his son ' Ba-cha-tahn ', the ' Dark One ', for the colour of his skin and because he was made at the dark of the moon ; and he told him that he must always remember that Ba-cha-tahn was not the equal of Ka-ru-in, because the darkness must always bow before the light.

Then Ka-ru-in showed his new companion the bison he had made, and rejoiced in the praise and admiration for which he had longed. And he made a lot of new animals, large, but carelessly drawn because he was in a hurry further to impress his son.

Finding that it was size and fierceness which most impressed Ba-cha-tahn, Ka-ru-in took little pleasure in the finer work required for a flower petal or the delicate feathers of an oriole. He was persuaded to make horrible birds, with leathern wings which creaked in flight like trees complaining in a high wind. He made monstrous animals which lumbered through the swamps, and the pits left by their feet were so deep that a deer could fall into them and break her leg ; and their necks were so long that they browsed off the tops of the trees, which began to wither. But when Ka-ru-in commanded his monsters to grow smaller they took no notice of him, for in his haste he had forgotten to give them any ears. When two of them met, they fought until one died ; for in his pride Ka-ru-in had forgotten to give them any kindliness.

Then, although Ka-ru-in could not change the monsters, he found a change in himself. Each day he found that he ran less swiftly than he had run yesterday. When he went uphill his heart pounded in his chest until he had to pause to catch his breath; while Ba-cha-tahn strode effortlessly past him looking back over his shoulder to grin at the discomfiture of his creator.

Ka-ru-in deliberately kept away from his Father, pretending that he was too busy looking after all the things he had made, for he would not admit, even to himself, that he was too ashamed to go home. Every day he grew more tired, and only drove himself to further efforts because he was afraid of his companion's taunts when he had to rest. He tried to leave Ba-cha-tahn, but even when he hid in the forest the Dark One always found him; for he was so swift, so tireless.

At last Ka-ru-in had to beg a favour of the man he had created: 'I long for solitude as once I longed for a companion,' he said. 'I will make you free of the Earth—and it is so wide a place that even I have explored only a small part of it, if you will leave me one small valley in which to be at peace.'

'Gladly will I leave you,' said Ba-cha-tahn scornfully, 'for you have become so very dull and tiresome that you are no fit companion for me.'

'Go, then,' said Ka-ru-in, for he was so weary that even his pride could not drive him to anger at this final taunt.

'I will go . . . but only on one condition.'

'I have granted you so many favours that one more can make no difference. Tell me what it is . . . then take it, and go.'

'The secret of the Words.'

'No! In my mouth they have brought enough sorrow: I shall never speak them again.'

'Then I shall stay here: to mock your infirmities; to remind you of your failures.'

'Why do you want to know the Words, when you admit that they have brought me nothing but failure, nothing but unhappiness?'

'Because in my mouth they will be put to better use than they ever were in yours.'

'Are there not enough monsters on Earth to content even you? Not a day passes without a battle between giants for you to watch. You love watching blood run, don't you Ba-cha-tahn—love it even more than I used to love clear water rippling in the sun?'

'I want a companion who can appreciate my pleasures, a companion like myself, who will not be squeamish as you have always been!'

The snake, who had been listening to their conversation, smiled; the cold, flat smile of reptiles.

'Grant him his wish, Ka-ru-in,' it said. 'Tell him the Words, so that he can be punished as you have been punished. A subtle revenge it will be: he will fight with the thing he creates even as his animals fight. They will kill each other, and Earth be free of them and their kind for ever.'

And Ka-ru-in listened to the voice of the snake, for it comforted him. So he told the Words to Ba-cha-tahn; who was so eager to use his new power that he left his creator without even troubling to bid him farewell. But Ka-ru-in was so glad to see him go that he was not disappointed even by this last ingratitude.

The snake slid out from the tree roots where it lived and rested its head on Ka-ru-in's knee. 'You have no time to rest, for you have a long journey to make before nightfall.'

'A journey? Why should I go on a journey?' said Ka-ru-in.

'To-morrow you will be more weary than you are to-day. To-morrow you may be too tired to travel so far.'

'But after I have rested I shall be strong again.'

'Not if you rest here,' said the snake. 'Only your Father can cure *your* weariness: you are growing old.'

'What is "old"? I never heard that word.'

'The result of mortality: a disease only your Father can cure. You must hurry, or you may not reach him in time.'

Then the snake flickered its tail and was gone. Ka-ru-in

got slowly to his feet, and took the path which led to the home of his Father.

He thought that the Lord of Earth would be surprised to see him, not realizing that his Father knew of all that had befallen him—all things, both great and small. The Father listened while his son spoke, and was glad that he omitted nothing, nor tried to excuse what he had done. At the end of the story Ka-ru-in said :

' Father, I have come to beg for your forgiveness, and to ask that you will cure me of being " old ". And above all things I implore you to make me forget the Words I should never have heard . . . so that I can never again desecrate them with my mouth.'

' I have never ceased to love you,' said the Father gently, ' and now that you have returned to me and again love me, you are already forgiven : for when two love each other that is another word for forgiveness of all things between them.'

' Then why are you sorrowful, Father, if you are no longer angry with me ? '

' Because now that you have come home . . . and I have been so lonely for you, I must send you on another journey.'

' Why must you send me away ? '

' I do not send you ; it is by your own choice that you go.'

' It is not my choice. . . . I want to stay with you always.'

' You chose to make the journey when you learned the secret Words. It is the law of the stars that one cannot create what one has not experienced.'

' But you have made plants, and rocks. . . . I have seen you do it ! '

' In my time I have been a rock, and a plant . . . until I became an animal that became a man, a man who became a god. But you, my son, were born of my spirit, not of your own timelessness. If you had been content with all that I gave you, you could have shared my immortality instead of seeking your own.'

' But how did I make the fish, and the snake, and the bison ? '

' You did not make them : I made them. That is why I

never told you the Words, for I knew that if you spoke them you would have to become all things that you created. For the Words were not your rightful heritage, nor will they be until you have made the long journey of becoming.'

' Must I be a monster ? '

' No ; for they were conceived by Ba-cha-tahn. You must be a man, Ka-ru-in. You are already a man, though not in all things. It is mortality which is making you weary : you are growing old, my son ; very old and tired.'

' Must I be black of skin and of heart as is Ba-cha-tahn ? ' said Ka-ru-in, despairing.

' No, you shall not be black. I have made an image of you in clay, for you must always be made in the substance of your own creation. But it is the red clay of the mountain tops, red with the reflection of the dawn, red with the fire-light that is stronger than the shadows, red as the mightiest of my trees.'

Then the Father kissed his son on the forehead, and on the breast, and on the feet, saying :

' Now sleep, my son ; and when you wake you shall open mortal eyes to which I shall be invisible. Yet always will you walk in my sight : even though you forget me I shall love you . . . and until your return to me I shall be lonely for you. Now sleep, my son. . . .'

Ka-ru-in lay back with his eyes closed, and a warmth and a peace enfolded him. The Father stood looking down at his sleeping son : in his hands the image of red clay.

Then the Lord of Earth whispered the secret Words : of which Red Man was born.

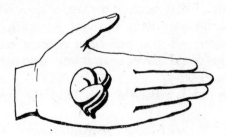

FIRST MAN : FIRST WOMAN

LONG ago, longer than a hundred generations of redwoods, a bear had a strange cub. She was used to cubs, having had five, but they had all grown up into very ordinary bears and then gone away to find a cave of their own. But *this* cub was hairless, except for a tuft on its head !

Mother Bear was not sure whether she ought to feel proud of him because of his strangeness, or feel ashamed because he was different : so, after telling her husband to look after him, she went up the mountain at dawn, to ask the Lord of Bears for advice.

She couldn't find the Lord of Bears, or perhaps he didn't answer her question because he wanted her to make up her own mind : so she came back to the cave, still uncertain what to do.

She found Father Bear basking in the sun, and the cub was scrambling over him, making a noise that was unknown to bears. The noise was laughter, so it was not surprising that it was unknown to bears, for laughter had not yet been heard on Earth.

And the strange cub was First Man !

'What did the Lord of Bears say to you?' asked Father Bear.

' I couldn't find him, but he couldn't have been angry with me, for on my way home I found a tree full of honey-comb and I ate a lot of it without being stung . . . but there is plenty left for you. So the Lord of Bears can't have been angry, can he ? '

' No,' agreed Father Bear, ' he can't even have been a little annoyed, or the bees would have stung you before you had eaten the first mouthful. Was it good honey-comb ? '

' Very good.'

' Then I think we must take that as a sign that this is a *fortunate* cub . . . he may even be the first of a new kind of bear. No doubt he will grow fur when he is older . . . anyway he seems very intelligent, and I like the sound he makes when I roll him over.'

The Bears were sorry that their new cub had such long hind legs that when he ran on all fours he moved clumsily, like a frog ; but when he grew older he stood upright much more often than the other cubs had done, so they were very proud of him. When he was too big to be suckled any longer,

they taught him where to find berries that were good to eat, and which should be avoided except when required for medicine : where to dig for the most succulent roots, and which trees had leaves or bark that satisfied hunger. He soon became clever at finding which hollow trees were likely to be full of honey-comb—though, as he was hairless, the bees stung him more often than they stung his parents.

They also taught him how to climb, and, in spite of his inadequate claws,

they soon found that he could climb faster and higher than they did, and could run out along branches which would not carry their weight. They didn't have to teach him to fight, for in those days when animals quarrelled, it only meant that when they chanced to meet they pretended not to have seen each other. Except for his fur, which to his mother's distress refused to grow, he developed more rapidly than any of his brothers and sisters, and by autumn he was as tall as his father, and never went on all fours except out of politeness to his parents. When the leaves began to fall, his Mother told him to eat as much as possible and not to run about too much, so that he could put on plenty of fat to keep him warm through the winter. When the first snows came they told him it was time to go into the cave to sleep through the cold.

First Man said he didn't want to sleep so long, but Father Bear told him, rather sharply, that bears who kept awake grew hungry, and that if they were foolish enough to go out into the whiteness to look for food they never found any, and sometimes died before they found their way back to the cave.

But First Man had grown tired of listening to the advice of his parents, so without letting them know what he was doing, he collected roots and nuts and honeycomb, and hid them in a hole under a boulder not far from the cave.

The morning when they saw that everything was covered with snow, Father Bear said to First Man :

' Lie down between your mother and myself, and then you'll be as warm as though you knew how to grow fur for yourself. Don't wriggle or you'll disturb my dreams : and, above all, don't wake us until the river shouts to you that Spring has returned.'

But First Man didn't believe his father, and he lay still only until he was sure that both his parents were fast asleep. Then he crept out of the cave, and though he found the snow too cold to be comfortable he didn't go home until it was dark. Every day he went out to explore the white world : but when he had finished his store of food he couldn't find any more . . . the thickets were barren of fruit and the roots were buried so deep under the snow that he didn't know where to dig. Feeling very hungry he went back to the cave, snuggled down between his parents, and tried very hard to go to sleep. But he woke as usual next morning, and though he prodded his Father, trying to wake him so that he could tell his son how to sleep until Spring, Father Bear only grunted and settled to his dreams again.

The more First Man tried to sleep the more hungry he became, until his hunger drove him out to search for food. Except for some pine needles, which made him feel sick, he found nothing to eat. A snow-hare sat up on its haunches and watched him plodding disconsolately through the drifts. First Man had cut his hand on a sharp rock and it was bleeding. He sucked the blood, and for a while it made him feel less hungry.

Then he thought, ' Perhaps bears can eat blood. I wonder if all animals have blood that is good to eat ? '

The snow-hare watched him come nearer. It was interesting to see a new kind of animal that had no fur, but of course it was not afraid . . . for in those days Fear was not known on Earth.

Almost without realizing what they were doing, First Man saw his hands break the neck of the snow-hare. He saw them take a sharp stone and slit up the belly : then his mouth was sucking greedily at the warm blood.

When he realized what he had done, he stood staring down at his blood-spattered hands and at the broken body of the hare staining the snow at his feet. He turned and fled down the mountain—trying to escape from the horror that was himself and from the first animal to be killed for food.

He knew that if he returned to his parents they would no longer accept him as their cub : they would smell the blood on his hands and know that he had betrayed them and the Lord of Bears. On and on he ran through the white stillness, and on the lower slopes of the mountain he paused : for a sound which to him was terrible came on the wind. It was the voice of the river ; calling to all the animals that the ice had broken, calling to them to awake for Spring had returned to them. And First Man knew that if he had had patience to learn the winter-sleep from his father, or had had the courage to curb his hunger even for another day, he would not have been outcast and alone.

Having betrayed his parents, he knew that the Lord of Bears would no longer listen to him. Then he thought, ' My mother told me that each kind of animal has a Great Lord who protects them : even the frogs have a Lord of Frogs, and the beetles a Lord of Beetles. Perhaps I am not a hairless bear . . . perhaps I am a new kind of animal which has a Lord of its own. He cannot be an *important* Lord, for otherwise I could not be such a failure . . . so perhaps he is as lonely as I am, and would listen even to me.'

So First Man climbed the mountain at dawn, as his mother had taught him to do ; and he shouted :

' My Lord ! . . . if anything so hairless and insignificant as myself has a Lord . . . please make another animal like me so that I can stop being so lonely.'

And a voice answered him : it was quite clear and

distinct, though he could not see where it came from, and it said :

'Now that you have remembered Me, you will not be alone any more. Cross the mountains into a new valley, and there you shall find First Woman.'

A Heron was sitting on her nest waiting for her husband to return from his evening flight. They had both been surprised when she had laid only one egg, instead of seven or more, and even more surprised when the egg itself had grown until it was all she could do to cover it with her wings to keep it warm.

'You are *sure* that you laid it yourself?' her husband had asked, not once but many times.

'Quite sure. And I have never left it unless you were on guard. So if another bird threw *my* egg out of the nest and laid another here, the fault is your's, not mine!'

'I have watched it the whole time you were away,' her husband assured her.

'Then stop being suspicious,' said Mother Heron severely. 'Personally I should prefer to hatch one very remarkable egg, such as this most certainly is, than a brood of ordinary chicks which any one could have laid!'

The chick, in spite of its size, did not seem very clever at cracking open the shell ; so as soon as she heard it tapping, Mother Heron helped it by gently breaking the egg with her beak.

The Herons were not surprised that First Woman had no feathers for they were used to their children being born naked. Herons at that time did not live on fish, and preferred a kind of water-weed, of which there was a plentiful supply in the lake where they had built their nest.

Father Heron spent most of the day wading in shallow water in search of tender shoots to tempt the appetite of his daughter. She never seemed to appreciate his offerings, but she ate them because there was nothing else. Though she grew with remarkable rapidity, her parents saw, to their great distress, that feathers showed no sign of sprouting. First

Woman could soon scramble over the edge of the nest, but it was a long time before she could stand upright . . . and even then she had none of the dignity usual to Herons. She liked playing in the water, and her parents were surprised to see that although she could not fly, having no feathers, she learned to swim without any difficulty. This caused Father Heron further anxiety.

'You don't think she is a kind of *duck*,' he said. 'You are sure that a duck . . . while I was away, at dusk . . .' Then he saw the reproachful look on his wife's face and added hastily, 'No, no . . . I am sure she is not a duck . . . I must apologize for making so foolish a remark.'

Mother Heron accepted his apology, but she didn't speak to him for the rest of the day.

Later in the year, Mother Heron decided she would build a new nest before laying again ; she had come to believe that it must have been something about the nest which had made the egg behave so curiously. Yes, she would build a new nest on the small island in the middle of the lake. It would have to be the largest she had ever made, for her daughter showed no sign of being able to fend for herself, so she would have to stay with her even after the new eggs were hatched. Still, her daughter had become quite useful in collecting water-weed . . . if only she would grow some feathers they could feel very proud of her.

Mother Heron gave her daughter many lessons in nest building.

'Always remember,' she said, 'that only *inferior* animals are content to live in a hole in the ground, or a cave. *We* always build our home. Make sure the sticks are carefully placed . . . choose them well, and line them with . . .' she was going to say, 'with feathers', but fearing to hurt her daughter's feelings, said instead, 'with dry grass, or anything suitable you can find.'

When the new nest was finished, Mother Heron laid an egg. She watched it anxiously for a few days, but it showed no signs of growing, so, reassured, she settled down and laid six more. She sat on them proudly and contentedly for a while, then one day, when her husband had been away longer than usual and she wanted to stretch her legs, she accepted her daughter's offer to look after the eggs.

When she came back to the nest she found a terrible disaster. First Woman had sat on the eggs, as she had seen her mother do. All of them were broken and the dead bodies of chicks, who so soon would have been ready to hatch, were lying pitifully among the crushed shells.

Distraught as was Mother Heron, her first thought was to protect her large and clumsy daughter from Father Heron's wrath.

'You must go away,' she said. 'You are quite old enough to look after yourself. You know how to build a nest and where the best water-weed can be found.'

'I can't go away,' said First Woman sadly. 'You have often told me that no Heron can fend for itself until it can fly . . . and how can I fly when I have no feathers?'

'You must have some of mine,' said Mother Heron, and she started to pull out some of her best feathers. 'Put these on your naked wings . . . stick them on with mud, and then stand up and flap . . . and don't be frightened when you feel yourself rising into the air.'

The mud wouldn't stick the feathers on First Woman's arms, so she stood up with a bunch of them in each hand ; flapping them obediently, but with very little hope that she would be able to fly.

It was then that Father Heron returned, and when he saw his seven children lying dead, and his poor wife with her wings raw and bleeding where she had plucked out her feathers, he wished that he was a thunder-cloud with a voice loud enough to express his indignation.

'One thing I must do,' he decided, 'and that at once. I must remove this horrid fledgling from the nest . . . carry it away, far away where it can never come back to make my poor wife sorrowful again.'

He swooped down and picked up First Woman by her hair. Mother Heron stood on the edge of the nest, flapping her ravaged wings mournfully, as she watched her husband

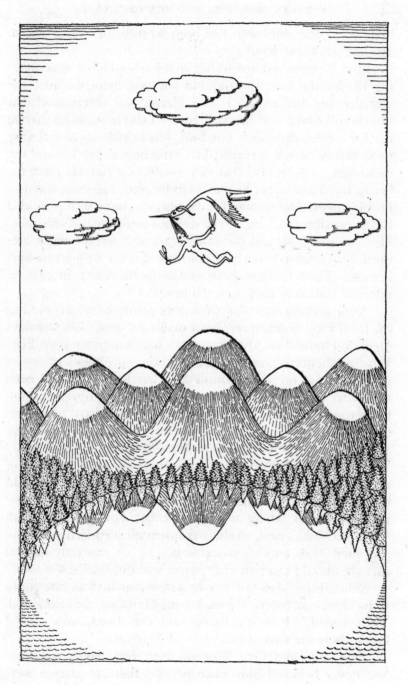

carry away the child who had been so difficult, yet of whom she had grown so fond.

First Woman did not realize that Father Heron was carrying her by the hair, she thought she was flying because she was flapping her arms. Father Heron was determined that she should never find her way back to the nest, so he carried her for a great distance. His beak was beginning to feel very tired before he saw a small lake in the new valley beyond the mountain. He decided that this would be a suitable place for her to build a nest, for he was a kindly bird, and even when so deeply angered he wanted his daughter to be as well provided for as possible, so long as she did not again disturb his wife. He swooped low, and did not let go of First Woman's hair until he was sure that she would not fall far enough to hurt herself. Then he flew away as fast as he could, in case he relented and went back to fetch her.

After making sure that there was plenty of water-weed in the lake, First Woman set about making a nest. On wet days Mother Heron had always spread her wings to give First Woman shelter : now it began to rain, so instead of laying the sticks flat on the ground in a circle, as she had been taught to do, First Woman set some of them upright, tying them together at the top with a strand of her hair. Between the upright sticks she threaded dry rushes to keep out the rain. So the first Tepee was made by First Woman.

When she had finished building, she saw something moving towards her through the reeds. Her Mother had told her that when a fledgling is full grown it flies away to a new nesting-ground where it finds another young heron with whom to build a nest, so she was not at all surprised when she saw First Man walking towards her . . . it was only natural that she should meet another heron-without-feathers.

When First Man saw her he knew that he was not going to be alone any more. ' Thank you, My Lord,' he said aloud. Then added, ' I should have said *Our* Lord, now that I know there are two of us.'

First Man and First Woman were very happy together. She never believed him when he said that his parents were

bears who lived in a cave, but, being First Woman, she pretended that she did, for she knew it would only annoy him if she insisted that they were both herons-without-feathers.

She thought that feathers had once grown from his hands, for when they met there was blood on them, like the blood on Mother Heron's wings when she had plucked them to give the power of flight to her daughter. But when First Woman mentioned the blood she saw that it distressed him and thought that this was because he was shy of being praised for his sacrifice. She washed the blood from his hands, and he was surprised to see that it came off so easily : he had scoured them many times with water and sand, but nothing he could do alone would take away the stain of the snow-hare he had killed.

She told him that she could fly, and when he would not believe her she thought he wanted to pretend that no one could fly, because he had given away his feathers and could no longer fly himself. So she took her mother's feathers from the place where she had hidden them and threw them away . . . so that she would not be tempted to enjoy flight that her husband could not share.

Sometimes she told him of the hills and valleys she had seen on her journey to the place of their meeting, but she did not often speak of it after she found that news of distant places made him restless, for she was content to stay where they had built their nest.

They had many children, who were born naked as their parents ; and all of them grew up to honour Their Lord.

Though First Man and First Woman never knew it, to each kind of animal a man or a woman was born, and these also had children. The tribes who are descended from them never forget to honour their First Ancestor, and a man who kills one of his totem animals is accounted to have killed his father, even to this day.

Why the Lord of Men, in his wisdom, found it necessary to allow children to be born to the Carrion Crow, from whom the Black Feathers are descended ; to the Rattlesnake, to the Bat, and to the Horned Lizard, is beyond the comprehension of all other tribes, though humbly they may say that it seems to have been an unfortunate decision.

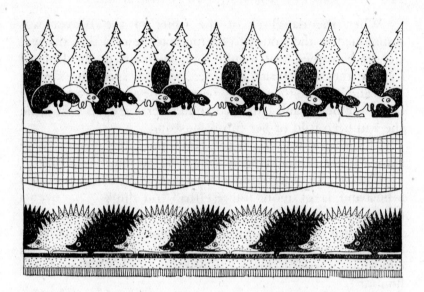

THE BEAVER AND THE PORCUPINE

THE Tribe of the Beaver and the Tribe of the Porcupine were strangers, for their hunting-grounds were divided by a range of barren hills. They never visited each other, for the Porcupines believed the Beavers to be a dull and plodding people, interested only in weaving blankets and making cooking-pots . . . certainly no worthy companions for warriors : while the Beavers thought the Porcupines were so timid that they spent most of their time building stockades to protect themselves from imaginary enemies . . . certainly entirely unsuitable friends for mighty hunters.

So both the Chief of the Beaver and the Chief of the Porcupine were very surprised to find how much they liked each other when they met for the first time at the Gathering of the Tribes, which took place every seven years. Before the end of the three days' feasting they liked each other so much that they decided their people must be united by a blood-tie without delay. One chief had an only daughter, the other an only son, so without consulting their children, they arranged for them to be married at the next full moon.

When the daughter of the Chief of the Beaver was summoned to the Council of Elders, to be told that she was already betrothed and would soon be married, she listened to what they had to say, and then, without speaking, she left them and went to the squaws' tepee. The squaws had already heard the news, and clustered round her, eager to hear what she had been told of her future husband.

'I did not wait to hear about him,' she said. 'Why should I listen to news which can hold no interest for me ? '

One of the older women chuckled. 'You will find that a husband is of more interest than you think . . . even a proud squaw learns that before long ! '

'I shall never marry a Porcupine,' said the Chief's Daughter. 'When I take a husband he will be of my own choosing, a young brave of our own tribe whom I can honour ! '

'But your father has made a promise in your name ! ' they exclaimed . . . horrified at this defiance of their Chief's wishes.

'Then he can break it ! ' she said calmly. 'Or if he dare not, he can send the Porcupines one of you in my place . . . though even if she were half-witted she would still be too good for them ! '

When the Chief heard of his daughter's defiance he first tried to reason with her, and when this produced no result he became very angry, and had her shut up in a stockade, which had been built for the safe-keeping of hostages who refused to promise not to escape.

The spaces between the logs were filled with mud plaster, but through the roof, whose beams were set too close for any one to climb out, the Chief's Daughter could see that the sky was hidden by clouds which promised heavy rain before evening. To show that she wasn't frightened, she said aloud :

'I will freeze, and I will starve, and they can keep me shut in here until I am an old, old woman. But I will *never* marry a Porcupine ! '

Food was brought to her once a day ; not much of it, but enough to keep her from feeling too hungry. It rained most

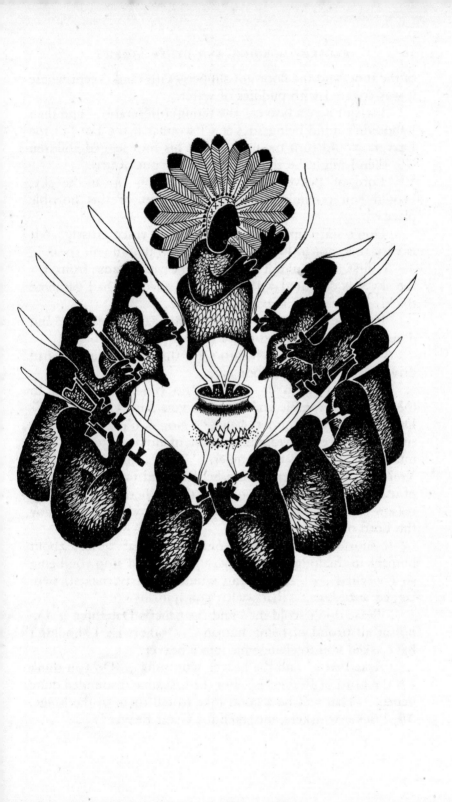

of the time, and the floor got slippery with mud except where it was covered with puddles of water.

' I wish I *were* a beaver,' she thought miserably, ' and then I shouldn't mind being so wet.   I wonder if the Lord of the Beavers would turn me into one of his four-legged children . . . then I might be able to dig my way out of here.'

' Lord of Beavers ! ' she said, looking up at the sky, ' could you possibly help me to get out of this horrible place ? '

' Don't stare up at the roof ! ' said a voice crossly. ' It is very rude not to look at the person to whom you speak ! '

At first she couldn't see where the voice came from, for the sky was coloured with sunset and shadows had gathered thickly between the log walls.

' Help me move some of this earth ' said the voice, ' and don't stand there staring like a broody water-hen ! '

A beaver heaved itself into sight through a tunnel it had driven up through the floor.

' So you want to be a beaver, do you ? ' it said, still in the same disagreeable voice. ' Can you do anything useful ? Dig, build, swim under water ? No, don't answer ! ' it snapped before she had time to think of anything to say which might put it in a better temper. ' Typical human you are ! You think the Beavers would be delighted to make you one of us. You look on us as your " little brothers ", but the only reason you never kill us is because you know it would annoy the Lord of Beavers.'

It snorted, ' I wish you could hear what we say about humans in the lodges sometimes : that would stop you being so conceited . . . if anything would ! Nasty, naked, two-legged *mistakes* . . . that's what you humans are ! '

' Please don't scold me ' said the Chief's Daughter. ' I'm not at all proud of being human . . . otherwise I shouldn't have asked you to change me into a beaver.'

' Asked *me* ? ' said the beaver scornfully. ' Do you think *I'm* the Lord of Beavers ? ' For the first time it sounded quite genial. ' That will be a good joke to tell them in the lodge. *Me*, Prickle-whiskers, mistaken for Great Beaver ! '

' Then why did you come when I called ? '

' I didn't come, I was sent ; *He* sent me. He told me to bring you to Him. Hurry up now, you mustn't keep Him waiting. Hold on to my tail and then you won't lose your way in the dark.'

As soon as the Chief's Daughter took hold of the tail, the beaver grew until it was the size of a large grizzly, and the tunnel it had made was suddenly large enough for her to walk upright without bumping her head on the roof. The tunnel made several sharp turns before sloping steeply down, and she heard a dull roaring noise which she realized was the sound of the river far above them.

' We are nearly there,' said Prickle-whiskers. ' Don't ask for anything you don't want or you may not like it when you get it . . . and don't say I didn't warn you ! Let go of my tail and walk straight ahead . . . and don't forget to be very humble, for you are about to see Great Beaver.'

The Chief's Daughter found herself in a cave, down which streamed a light, so dazzling that she had to shut her eyes. When she opened them she found it very easy to be humble : the cave was so high and she was so small—so small in front of the great figure from which came the light. Was it a Man or a Beaver ? Of this she was never sure, for the light He gave forth made it impossible to see His face except as a warmth and a glory.

' Ask and it shall be granted,' said His voice.

' O Great Beaver, I most humbly beseech you that now I may cease to be in human shape and become an ordinary beaver.'

' Instead of an ordinary human ? ' asked the voice.

She was just going to say, ' I am *not* an ordinary human, I am the daughter of a Chief ! ' when she remembered to whom she was speaking, and said, ' Instead of a *very* ordinary human.'

' The wish is granted ! ' said His voice.

Then the brilliant light faded, and the cavern shrank to the size of a cave such as beavers make for themselves in the river bank. The Chief's Daughter looked down at her hands ; they had strong claws and were covered in soft brown fur.

'I *am* a beaver!' she said in an awed voice.

'Of course you are a beaver,' said Prickle-whiskers, who was standing beside her. 'And you had better come and learn how to be a *useful* beaver, or no one will want you in their lodge.'

Perhaps if one has been born a beaver there is nothing monotonous in gnawing through logs all day, nor does it make your teeth ache : but the Chief's Daughter found it disagreeable. The beavers working on each side of her seemed to find it as easy as gnawing maize off the cob, and perhaps they liked the taste of wood. Prickle-whiskers had explained that she was inexperienced, so they pretended not to notice how slow she was, and said her mistakes didn't matter.

Prickle-whiskers gave her water-lily roots for supper. She thanked him very politely, and was relieved to find they were easy to chew. When their day's work was finished he took her to one of the larger lodges where beavers meet for conversation. At first she found it very interesting to listen to them, but they repeated the same jokes night after night, and told stories which must have been stale for several generations. The stories were usually about dams they had built in the past; how high they were, how many trees had been needed to make them. The young male beavers talked of diving, and the women beavers discussed their children, or grumbled about their husbands . . . though always with affection.

No one took any interest in the Chief's Daughter, and when she tried to join in the conversation they stared at her as though they were deaf. Actually they didn't understand her when she talked about her life as a human, and she didn't know anything of the subjects which interested them. Beavers never listen unless they know they are likely to be interested in what they are going to hear, and they are so industrious that they never have time to be bored; which is why they live so peacefully together.

At last the Chief's Daughter got so tired of living in a lodge that she decided to go away and live by herself . . . even though that would mean leaving Prickle-whiskers of whom she had grown fond.

'I shall be able to find myself a hole under the bank to live in,' she thought. 'And now that I am so good at looking after myself I need never go hungry . . . so I shall be able to manage quite well alone.'

So one morning at dawn she swam away up-stream.

When the Chief found that his daughter had disappeared, he refused to believe that she had been aided by a spirit, and he said that one of the women must have helped her to escape, which accounted for the stockade being still fastened on the outside. To try to prove this, he questioned each of the women in turn, and their indignant denials only increased his conviction of the secrecy of women.

He was determined that the disobedience of his daughter should not spoil the alliance with the neighbouring tribe, so, although two of the Elders in Council disapproved of the plan, he decided to adopt a girl and to send her to the Porcupines in place of his real daughter. He expected that all the girls of suitable age would be anxious to receive so great an honour, until, to his great annoyance, they one by one refused to acknowledge him as their new father. They phrased their refusals most politely, saying that they were unworthy for such consideration, but the politeness was only the moss on the hard rock of their determination.

It was then that the Chief remembered a child who had been found wandering in the forest some years ago. She was half-witted, blind in one eye, and her right foot splayed out so that she walked with a limp. She was looked after by the old squaws, for it was obvious that no man would ever ask for her in marriage.

' She will have to be my daughter,' thought the Chief regretfully. ' It will be most unsatisfactory, but better than abandoning the whole plan. I hope that her nature is as disagreeable as her appearance, for then, during the short time which must elapse between her adoption and her marriage, she will certainly make things most uncomfortable for the other girls . . . and most richly they deserve it ! '

So Pokoo, which was the poor creature's name, suddenly found herself the centre of attention. Instead of having a discarded tunic as her only garment, she was clothed in soft doe-skin ; she had fine pelts to sleep on, and embroidered moccasins for her feet. Her tangled hair was combed and plaited with coloured strands . . . but in spite of all this her appearance remained sadly unprepossessing.

The Chief of the Porcupine had told his son that his future bride was renowned for her beauty and intelligence, so the young man looked eagerly forward to the day when she would arrive with her father for the two days' feasting which would precede the marriage ceremony.

The horror he felt when he saw Pokoo can well be imagined, and only the self-control indispensable to all who undergo the ordeals required of a warrior made it possible for him to conceal his feelings. But when the Beavers had withdrawn for the night he entered his father's tepee like an angry thunder cloud :

' Why did you tell me that the Beaver's daughter was

beautiful ? ' he demanded.   ' She is hideous to look at, and so
stupid that it was foolish of the gods to provide her with a
tongue that can talk ! '

'You must not be too hasty in your judgement,' said the
Chief defensively; 'and, after all, looks are not everything. . . .'

'No doubt a blind man would find her less repulsive than
I do . . . if he was deaf as well, and so could remain oblivious
to her appalling stupidity.'

'She may only be shy,' said the Chief; and before his son
could answer, added, ' shyness in a woman is no disadvantage
. . . does the hunter enjoy a quarry which comes trotting
towards him ? '

'If she came trotting towards *me*, I should run away
faster than I have ever run before ! '

'A warrior *never* runs away,' said the Chief reproachfully.
'I admit that she contributed little to the conversation, but
I assure you, my son, that it is better to have a squaw who

talks too little than one who continually disturbs one's thoughts by her idle chatter.'

' Did you notice how her eye leered in the fire-light ? '

' I am disappointed that you should speak so discourt-eously of your future wife.'

' She is *not* my future wife ! ' shouted the young man, leaping to his feet. ' And nothing you can do will make me change my mind ! '

' Be silent ! ' shouted the Chief. ' I have pledged my word in your name and you cannot betray the tribe.'

' You lied to me . . . you told me she was beautiful and intelligent ! If you can lie to your son, why can't you lie to the Beavers ? Tell them that I am dead . . . that I am mad . . . tell them what you like, but convince them that I will never marry the Chief's Daughter ! '

' You will obey me, or become an outcast ! '

' Then there is nothing left to do except to bid you farewell,' said the young man coldly.

' Yes, there is ! I forbid you to go ! And if you try to run away I shall send trackers to fetch you back. Then you will be given the choice for the last time . . . the choice between marriage, or death ! Have I made myself understood ? You may go now, and return to me at dawn.'

The Chief's Son knew that his father had a ruthless streak in his character which would force him to carry out his threat, even though it broke his heart. He went and climbed an out-crop of rock, and sat there in the starlight trying to think what to do. He heard a rustle in the undergrowth, and look-ing down, saw a porcupine trotting along the path below him.

' I wish it was the Lord of Porcupines instead of just an ordinary one,' he said aloud. To his intense astonishment, the porcupine stopped, looked up at him, and said :

' I'll take a message to Him if you wish.' Then, as the Chief's Son was too startled to answer, the porcupine repeated in a louder voice, ' I said, I'll take a message to Him if you wish ! '

' This must be a dream,' said the Chief's Son to himself.

' Nonsense ! ' said the porcupine briskly, ' of course it

isn't a dream. If you are going
to be so stupid it is no use me
wasting my time. But don't
say I didn't offer help when you
asked for it ! '

The young man slid down
the rock and landed with a thud
by the porcupine. ' You are
real and you can talk,' he said
in an awed voice.

' Put your hand on my quills
if you still have any doubts . . .
you can't draw blood by touch-
ing an *imaginary* porcupine,' it
said scornfully.

The young man did as
he was told, and then drew
back, sucking his hand where
the quills had pierced the skin.

' Serves you right for being
so disbelieving,' it said. ' Now hurry up and give me your
message, I can't stand here all night chattering to a half-witted
human.'

' I've got to marry a woman who is horribly repulsive
or else be put to death . . . and I don't want to do either.'

' Very reasonable, so why don't you run away ? '

' Warriors can't run away,' said the Chief's Son regretfully,
' or else they are for ever dishonoured.'

' Nonsense ! ' said the porcupine. ' If you don't like one
place, go to find another ; that's only reasonable.'

' Even if I *did* go the trackers would soon find me.'

' They wouldn't if you had a long enough start of them
. . . especially as its going to rain to-morrow.'

' I wouldn't have a start. I think I am being watched, and
they would follow me as soon as I had left the encampment.'

' Would seven days' start be enough ? '

' More than enough . . . but it's quite impossible.'

' Nothing is impossible if you know how to do it,' said

the porcupine severely. 'Go and collect everything you want to take with you. Come here just before dawn and start climbing that hill . . . and I'll see that no one follows you.'

'But how can you manage that?' asked the Chief's Son doubtfully.

'How should I know? But Great Porcupine will find it quite easy . . . nothing is too difficult for *Him*.'

The porcupine rattled its quills impatiently. 'Hurry up now and do what you are told . . . take as much as you can carry, for you won't have to travel fast.'

So the Chief's Son did as he was told, and at dawn he was back at the rock but there was no sign of the porcupine. He climbed up the hill, and when he came to the crest he looked down on the encampment, which was set on a grassy plateau surrounded by woods. Floating up to him on the still morning air came a shout . . . and he knew that his flight had been discovered.

'What a fool I have been not to climb faster,' he thought, 'for then I should have a better chance to get away.'

He was just going to start running, when he saw sudden confusion break out in the encampment . . . people scurrying backwards and forwards shouting to each other. From every side of the green open space a moving stockade was closing in on them . . . hundreds and hundreds of porcupines were walking slowly backwards with their quills outspread. Three deep were their ranks, too wide for any man to jump; an impassable barrier of animals, which could not be attacked for they were the totem of the tribe!

'Very nicely done indeed!' said a voice, and the Chief's Son saw that the porcupine was sitting beside him. 'It was quick work getting them all there in time, but Great Porcupine sent out a general call, so they travelled all night.' 'Pretty sight, isn't it?' it added complacently; 'all those quills shining in the morning light. They won't move for seven days, so you can make your journey at a comfortable pace . . . and if you should meet a porcupine on your way don't forget to thank it for the help we have been to you.'

'I won't forget,' said the Chief's Son fervently. Then, with a last glance at his imprisoned tribe, he went on his journey.

On the evening of the seventh day he came to a wide river, and decided that it would be a good place in which to pass the night. He built a fire and over it roasted a pigeon that he had brought down with a stone from his sling during the afternoon.

The Chief's Daughter was getting very tired of living alone. She had found a dry and comfortable hole under the bank, and there was plenty of food near the river so she never went hungry : but she had no one to be fond of, and no one to be fond of her. She was sitting on the bank, combing her whiskers with her forepaws, when she saw a cooking-fire twinkling in the distance. Very naturally she was not afraid of fire, so she slid into the water and swam up-river to investigate.

The Chief's Son was also feeling lonely, so when he saw a beaver peering at him from the edge of the circle of firelight, he threw some food towards it to encourage it to come closer. This action showed the Chief's Daughter that she had been fortunate enough to meet a man who was fond of beavers, so she went up to him, rested her head on his knee, and gazed up at him with her large and beautiful eyes. The young man found himself strangely moved at this act of confidence from a beaver, for he had always believed them to be shy and unsociable animals.

During the next few days he was even more delighted to find that it had no intention of leaving him, and that even when he slept it curled up beside him like a faithful dog. Unfortunately he could not understand Beaver, which was all the Chief's Daughter could speak, but by gesture and with her eloquent eyes, she tried to make it clear to him that both as a beaver and as a human she had fallen in love.

'My little beaver,' he said, stroking her soft deep fur. 'You have listened most patiently while I have told you the story of my travels, and I really believe you have understood

4

every word I said. I couldn't have married a hideous woman, could I ? '

The Chief's Daughter shook her head vigorously, and the young man smiled. ' I knew you understood. You are so clever, my beaver. If only you were in human shape you would be all I could hope to find in a wife. . . . You are beautiful and intelligent, lovely and brave. We should never weary of each other's company . . . would you marry me if you were a human ? '

The Chief's Daughter nodded her head, as, trembling with love, she accepted his proposal. She had forgotten she was only a beaver, until she tried to put her arms round his neck, and saw that they ended in paws, with strong claws made specially for digging. She shook with sobs, and tears rolled out of her eyes. He thought she was shivering with cold, so he wrapped her in his robe and went to heap more wood on the fire.

Prickle-whiskers, though the Chief's Daughter had never noticed him, had not let her out of his sight since she left the lodge. He had been scornful of her as a human, but since she had been a beaver he had come to love her dearly. He was always making up stories to himself of how one day she would be lonely without him, or fall into danger from which he would rescue her, so that she would discover that she loved him. He decided that instead of returning to the lodge they would go to the hole under the bank he had already prepared, and there, in time, they would have so many children and grandchildren that they would build their own dam.

Prickle-whiskers could hear all that she was saying, in Beaver, to the Chief's Son. ' I love you and will always love you ! If only I was human again I could make you so happy, but even though I am only a beaver I shall never leave you until I die ! '

These words shattered Prickle-whisker's dreams for the future as a reflection in still water is shattered when a heavy stone is thrown into the pool. Silently he slid into the river, swimming as fast as he could in search of Great Beaver.

'Yes, Prickle-whiskers,' said Great Beaver. 'What do you want?'

'I want you to turn the human I once brought to you back into a human.'

'Why should I change her again? I told her she would have to remain a beaver if I granted her wish.'

'She has not forgotten that,' said Prickle-whiskers earnestly. 'For if she had not remembered she would have tried to find you herself.'

'Then why have you come to me?' asked Great Beaver gently.

'You said that one day you would grant me a wish . . . because I had been your faithful messenger.'

'That is true,' said Great Beaver. 'What is your wish?'

'That *her* wish shall be granted.'

Prickle-whiskers was almost sure that her wish would be to become human again, but he still hoped, even though he would not admit it to himself, that her real wish would be to raise a family of beavers with Prickle-whiskers as their father.

So he swam up-river, and when he saw the glow of a cooking-fire reflected in the water he climbed up the bank. . . . And the last of his dreams for the future melted like a splinter of ice in hot embers.

The Chief's Daughter was again human, and very beautiful : and she was asleep in the arms of the Chief's Son.

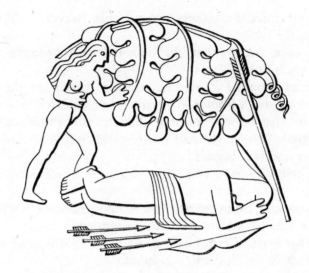

THE ARROW OF THE GREAT HUNTERS

BEYOND the memory even of the grandfathers, there lived
a mighty warrior called Pa-ha-chi. None could equal him
at wrestling or with the bow, so there was sorrow through-
out the circle of tepees, when, in fighting a grizzly, he was
crippled. Now since Pa-ha-chi became lame he had become
also a dreamer of dreams : but of this he told no one, fearing
to hear a mocking voice say, ' Pa-ha-chi the Warrior has
become a story-teller, without first waiting to be one of the
Old Men ! '

There had been peace for many years in that valley, so
no watchers were posted on the boundaries, and when the
companions who had once honoured Pa-ha-chi as their leader
went to the distant hunting grounds he was the only one to
be left with the squaws. Sadly he watched them take the path
to the hills, and then he lay down under a pine tree, hoping
in sleep to forget his loneliness.

He dreamed that he was standing at the head of the pass
which led to the western valley : towards him advanced the
warriors of the Black Feathers. Still they came on, even
though it was over the bodies of those who had already been

slain by his arrows. Now his quiver was empty, and he called on the Great Hunters that they might come to his aid. Swift as an echo to his voice, an arrow stood quivering in the ground beside him . . . a strange arrow, such as he had never before seen. He plucked it from the earth and fitted it to his bow-string. . . .

Then the thread of his dream snapped, as a woman's voice called to him, ' Pa-ha-chi, Pa-ha-chi, I bring news of danger! I have seen the smoke of many fires beyond the western pass and heard the mutter of war-drums.'

Still half asleep, and speaking more to himself than to her, he said, ' If the Great Hunters give me their arrow I can protect you. . . .'

Silently the woman held out to him an arrow such as would be found only in the quiver of an Immortal. It was longer than a man could span with his arms, and the bow with which it could mate would be too powerful even for the mightiest warrior to bend.

' The arrow was upright behind your head,' said the woman. ' At first I thought it was a young tree and you were its shadow. Then I remembered that the sons of the Great Hunters are called the " Lords of the Arrow ", and knew that you have been chosen to protect us. So I shall keep the news of danger from the squaws, for there is no need for them to hide.' Then the woman went away, and Pa-ha-chi was alone with the arrow.

He addressed it with the honour accorded to the totem, saying, ' On the other side of sleep I am not a cripple, O honoured messenger of the Great Hunters. There I could wield a bow worthy to be your mate, but here I must petition you to find a more subtle use for my small strength.'

And the Arrow said to him, ' If you can answer my questions I will fight with you against the enemy, even though you hold no bow from which I can fly. Is the seed or the tree most to be honoured for its wisdom ? '

Pa-ha-chi answered, ' Both in their turn. The seed may say, ' I am the son of the Redwood, but I am only a seed, therefore I am less than my ancestors ". Or it may say, " I am the father of a forest, and therefore greater than any single tree, even though its branches sweep the sky ".'

' That is the answer I hoped to hear from you, and so my shaft can call you " brother ",' said the Arrow. ' Now answer my second question : Does the tallest mountain, being so close to the sky, know what the stars are saying ? '

' Only when the stars remember that they were mountains and speak to them in the voice of a brother. The rocks cannot hear me unless I speak to them in the voice of the rock from whence I came.'

' Again you have given me the answer for which I hoped,' said the Arrow, ' so now my head as well as my shaft can call you " brother ". Here is my third question : If on a journey you came to a river too wide to swim and you were wise in your generations ; would you peel the bark from a tree to make yourself a canoe, or wait for the beavers to build a dam by which you might cross ? '

' If I were wise in my generations I should have no need to do either : for I could again become a bird, and so my body, having recaptured the power of flight which is now possessed only by my thoughts, would reach the far bank before the first ring of bark could be cut, or the most industrious of beavers be able to collect more than a few twigs.'

' For the third time you have given me the answer I hoped to hear ! ' said the Arrow. ' Now can my feathers also call you " brother ", and I am able to assist you to overcome this arrogant tribe, whose presence in these valleys is not in accordance with the wishes of the Great Hunters who sent me to you as their messenger. Before attacking an enemy it is always wise to consider his weakness, so that the value of your own strength can be accurately judged. The Black Feathers, although they are excellent warriors, have few wise men among them, and so they have become unduly credulous of omens. Were a bird, for instance a Cardinal, to circle their encampment seven times and then to alight on their totem, I am sure they would consider it a sign of such unusual import that they would follow it without question.

'To be able to receive a messenger of the Great Hunters, such as myself, one must first have sufficient experience to see nothing extraordinary in such an occurrence; secondly, one must know that all such messengers ask questions which must be answered as a proof of mutual integrity. But the Black Feathers have not this knowledge, and often ascribe meanings to events which do not concern them, being self-centred, arrogant, and at times quite absurdly credulous.

'Therefore, my brother, when you have circled their encampment seven times and then alighted on their totem, you will wait until they have brought their Chief before you . . . which they will certainly do, as any other course would not be in accordance with their traditions. You will then fly southwards, alighting now and then so as to give them a chance to keep up with you . . . a chance of which I am sure they will avail themselves. Should you become unsure in which direction to lead them, you have only to ascend to a height sufficient to allow you to see beyond the next ridge of hills. You will observe there a deep and narrow canyon which they will be unable to cross. When you have led them to it, and so fulfilled the first part of these instructions, you will find me beside you, ready to offer further advice. . . Is there anything you wish me to repeat, any point which I have not made clear?'

'Each word you have spoken I have most faithfully remembered,' said Pa-ha-chi, 'but there is still one small

matter . . . so small that it is hardly worth mentioning. How
am I to turn myself into a Cardinal ? '

' Take the feathers from my shaft,' said the Arrow. ' Put
two in your forehead-thong, one in the loop of each of your
sandals, and hold the fifth and the sixth in your right hand and
in your left. I advise you that before doing so you must face
in the direction of your enemies, so that, as a Cardinal, you
will not waste time in flying east when you wish to progress
westwards.'

When Pa-ha-chi took the sixth feather in his hand he felt a
dark whirling sensation, which he had previously only experienced when diving to the bottom of a pool so deep that
the feat had never before been attempted. Then the dark
whirling ceased ; and was followed by a sensation similar to
being carried down-stream by a swift, though kindly current.
He opened his eyes, to see, far below him, land flowing past ;
and discovered that the flight of a Cardinal is a most pleasant
way of getting from place to place.

When he reached the enemy encampment he saw that he
had not been unduly apprehensive either in regard to their
numbers or their intentions. All were warriors in full war-
paint, and with them were neither children nor squaws. No
one took any notice of him during his first two circles, but
during the third and fourth several men stared up at him. At
the fifth circle these upturned faces were joined by many
others, and by the time he alighted on their totem every

man within sight was staring at him with awe and amazement.

That night he slept on the totem pole, after enjoying the offerings of grain and shreds of dried meat, which they set before him in homage.

When at dawn they again assembled before him, he flew southwards; finding it as easy to make them follow him as it would have been for him to track a wounded deer across snow. On the third day he brought the three hundred warriors to the brink of the deep and narrow canyon, and as soon as they were encamped, he flew into the branches of a giant redwood, which grew on the edge of the cliff, to wait for the appearance of the Arrow.

The shaft of the Arrow, now of course without its feathers, so closely resembled the branch against which it rested that Pa-ha-chi did not see it until it spoke to him.

'You have done well, my brother. You have been the subtle warrior who makes the enemy turn his weapon against himself. It is true that a Cardinal took the same direction as did the Black Feathers, yet it was not the bird, but their own credulity which led them to this canyon. I have one more suggestion to make while you remain a bird. Again circle seven times round their encampment; then fly backwards and forwards across the canyon until they understand that you wish them to cross it also. Having done so, return to me . . . but take care when you alight upon this branch, for you will no longer have wings for support should you fall.'

Pa-ha-chi obeyed the Arrow, and on returning to the tree he found himself again in the body of a young warrior, to whom the ground looked so far away that had he not been used to heights it would have made him dizzy.

'To call on Gods who are in fact the Gods of your enemy is unwise,' said the Arrow, 'for such temerity arouses their intense displeasure. The Black Feathers claim not only their own Gods—the Dark Thunder, the Black Moon, the Rattlesnake, and the Bat—but also at times they invoke *our* elder brothers . . . and never seem to learn that this provokes the same response as a rattlesnake might receive if it demanded

kinship with the Lord of Bears. They even claim descent from the Lord of the Redwood, though I should have thought that the least intelligent of mortals knew that this honour belongs only to the children of the Great Hunters. It would be well for the enemy to learn how unwise it is to rely on a strength which does not belong to them by right, and that among the Gods also there are enemies as well as brothers. It is, as you have no doubt noticed, an evening so calm that no leaf stirs. Therefore if the tree in which we are sitting began to agitate its branches, I have every confidence that it would make a very proper impression on the men you have led here.'

' It is so great a tree,' said Pa-ha-chi, ' that even if I were not lame and could leap from branch to branch like a squirrel, I fear I could not make the branches move in a manner which would be in any way remarkable.'

' I did not suggest,' said the Arrow, ' that in the body of a man you should try to emulate a squirrel . . . for that would neither be dignified nor produce any useful result. However, were you to become this tree, and at the same time were to remember all that it and its brother trees have known of tempests before which forests bow down; were to listen to the screaming of the wind, and hear the thunder of mighty timbers which in their fall bring down ten centuries: remember it, Pa-ha-chi, until even though your long roots hold fast deep in the earth you, too, must fall before that wind. . . .'

Even the thought of being so far from the ground during a tempest such as the Arrow described made Pa-ha-chi feel giddy, but he said bravely :

' I shall most willingly do as you suggest if you think it will serve to vanquish our enemy.'

' You must take care to think only of tempests coming from the north-east, so as to ensure that when you fall it will be in the direction of the canyon.'

' It is a very deep canyon,' said Pa-ha-chi doubtfully. ' And what good will it do to our cause when this redwood, who will then be me, lies broken at the bottom of it ? '

' You underrate your stature,' replied the Arrow severely ;

'you will fall *across* not down the canyon : and your top-most branches will be driven into the firm ground on the far side. Your trunk is very wide ; three men could walk on it abreast. The Black Feathers will not hesitate to use it as a bridge . . . the bridge they will think has been provided for them by the Lord of the Redwood.

'I do not wish to appear unduly critical,' said Pa-ha-chi, 'but might it not have been better had I led them in some other direction ; thus avoiding the extra difficulty of having to aid them to cross the canyon ? '

'Only a few of them will *cross* the canyon : the tree which you will soon become is very old, and though it is unusual among the kingdom of the Redwood, its heart has long been dead, and for nearly a century has been inhabited by termites. When the Chief is in the middle of the bridge, you must put forth all your strength . . . till the great tree snaps like a twig, sending him, and we hope many of his followers, crashing to their death.'

'Though I am sure you have provided for every event-uality, would it be impertinent if I were to ask what will happen to *me* when the tree I have become breaks in accord-ance with my will ? '

'You will again be a warrior . . . and by that time I shall have thought of some further advice for you. Take my shaft in your hands. Hold it against your forehead, and say, " Brother ! I am your Brother ".'

Pa-ha-chi felt calm as the sky on a still evening, enduring as the White Mountains. The procession of years passed before him so swiftly that the flowers of high summer were seen against a background of snow, like brilliant beads on a chief's robe of white doe-skin. He longed to meditate upon this tranquil pattern of slow growth, but he remembered the words of the Arrow.

Out of the stillness he called on the wind, until he felt the shafts of driven rain assail him ; and he trembled as the sky split open to release the golden serpents of lightning . . . the most terrible enemy of forests. The memory of a thousand storms assailed his boughs . . . yet to the men sleeping at his

feet the air remained undisturbed even by a breeze. Yet
through the silence Pa-ha-chi, the Redwood, heard trees even
mightier than himself echo down the centuries their thunder-
ous fall. He felt his roots begin to relax their grasp on the
earth which had housed them for so long. . . .

In terror the Black Feathers sprang from their rest . . .
as against the brilliant processional of the stars they saw the
great tree falling in silence, until its highest branches crashed
down on the far side of the canyon.

But by morning they forgot the fears which had kept
them wakeful through the night. A few of them thought
that the torrential rains of the previous winter had washed
the earth from the roots, that it was only by chance that the
tree fell when they were there to see it; but these did not
voice their thoughts, for the Chief declared that the Lord of
the Redwoods had sent this tree, his servant, in answer to
their appeal.

They decided that they must cross the canyon on the
bridge so thoughtfully provided, yet the Chief preferred to
take the precaution of sending five of his warriors, the five
least favoured by him, to make sure that it was secure. When
he saw that the great trunk did not stir under their weight,
he himself set foot upon it.

Then did Pa-ha-chi put forth his strength, like a man
trying to break rawhide thongs which bind him prisoner.
And, as the Chief reached the centre of the bridge, it broke
beneath him. He, and a hundred of his followers, fell into
the abyss, and died.

Pa-ha-chi thought he was still the tree, or at least the part
of it whose roots still clung to the place of their long growth.
Then he found that he was again a man, a man hanging by
his hands from a ledge of rock some distance along the
canyon. Though he was lame he could still climb swiftly,
and without great difficulty he pulled himself up the cliff and
was soon lying on firm ground . . . panting a little from the
effort.

He looked round for the Arrow, but seeing no sign of
it he decided he must do what he could alone until was it

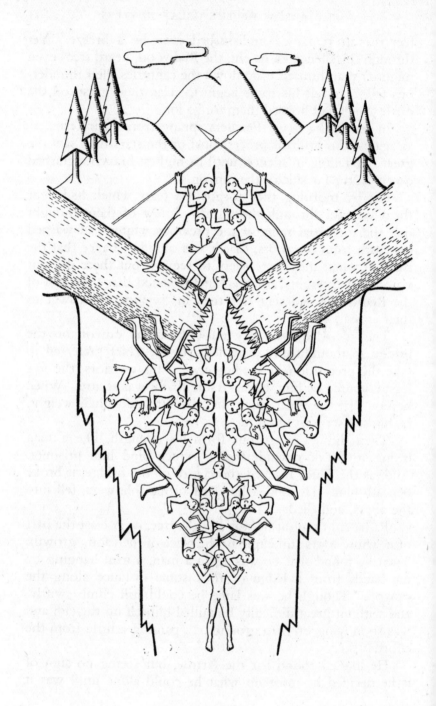

ready to offer him further advice. In the distance he heard the lamentations of those remaining warriors who had watched their Chief and many of their companions snared so rapidly by death. Taking care not to be seen, Pa-ha-chi crawled through the undergrowth until he was near enough to hear what they planned to do. It was as he expected : they decided that the omens had betrayed them and that the wisest course to take was to flee from a country which was clearly the haunt of demons.

Dejectedly the Black Feathers plodded along the path which they had so joyfully followed in the wake of the Cardinal. Pa-ha-chi followed them, though because of his lameness he found this arduous. On the sixth day they came to the first of the great caves by which the White Mountains that formed the southern boundary of the tribe were honey-combed. Pa-ha-chi knew of these caves for he had been there as a youth. Only the very brave would enter them, for many who did so never returned . . . some said they had lost them-selves, others that they had been seized by the demons which inhabit all places that are cut off from the light of the sun. There was a tradition, though none of the tribe believed in it, that the caves had another entrance on the far side of the mountains. Pa-ha-chi now saw that this tradition was true ; for in the outer cave were many pine torches, some of them half consumed, and when these were lighted by the Black Feathers, they showed blazes on the rock walls . . . marking a clear path through the mountains.

Pa-ha-chi dared not follow the enemy very far, for, having no torch, he could not have retraced his steps. Hidden in the shadows he listened to the plans they were making : some said they would never return this way, others that they would bring back many warriors to revenge the death of the Chief.

Pa-ha-chi knew that there was no other way by which the Black Feathers could again cross the mountains to threaten the peace of his tribe, but when he found his way back to the mouth of the cave he flung himself down and fell into despair. He thought the Arrow had deserted him, and that there was no way by which he could seal the mouth of the cave to prevent the return of the enemy. He was picking up stones and throwing them disconsolately into a nearby pool when he noticed that the seventh stone felt different to the rest . . . it was shaped like an arrow head : it *was* the Arrow head !

' So you have recognized me at last,' said the Arrow sharply. ' I have already given you my feathers and my shaft. How did you expect to recognize me without them if you did not trouble to look more carefully ? I was beside you on the first night of your journey here. . . . I even stuck into your ribs when you tried to sleep, but you never noticed me . . . presumably you took me for an ordinary stone ! '

' I am sorry, profoundly sorry,' said Pa-ha-chi. ' Is it too much to hope that in spite of my stupidity you will forgive me ? '

' No forgiveness required,' said the Arrow, ' you have already brought quite enough trouble on yourself for so small a discourtesy. Instead of my being able to provide you with a comfortable means of travel you have had to walk.'

' What else could I have done ? '

' I couldn't have turned you into a bird again,' said the Arrow, ' for you have used my feathers already . . . nor could you become a tree, for my shaft has gone. You would have had to be something in stone . . . like my head. I had thought of making you one of the stones they carry in their slings . . . stones they use for bringing down small birds. But now that the Black Feathers have gone you no longer have need of me.'

' But they might come back. You said you could turn me into a stone . . . would I have to be a small stone ? '

' Not very small. . . . How large would you want to be ? '

' Large enough to close the mouth of this cave for ever ; so that the enemy could never pass this way again.'

' I could do it, but it would be very difficult,' said the Arrow thoughtfully. ' It would take *all* of my head to make you so large, and once it was all used there would be nothing of me left to turn you back into a man again. If I were to turn you into such a stone, you would have to *remain* a stone. It would take a long time for a stone to grow into a warrior . . . more centuries than there are cones on a pine tree.'

' But the Black Feathers would never come back. . . .
There is no other way for them to cross the mountain ? '

' No other way,' said the Arrow. ' But isn't it too great a
sacrifice ? '

' Any warrior would die without question to protect the
tribe. Shall I, Pa-ha-chi, fail them because I have not the
courage to become a stone ? '

' Be very sure, Pa-ha-chi . . . be very sure ! To be a stone
will be like a long sleep with no bright dreams.'

' I am ready, my Arrow. I am ready to become a stone.
Will you call me brother when I am again a warrior ? '

As Pa-ha-chi took the head of the Arrow into his hand,
there came upon him a stillness more profound even than he
had known as a Redwood. Yet he who had thought to
become insentient almost for eternity found that he could fly
as he had not flown even as a Cardinal.

He was a warrior, yet he was no longer a man. For those
who now called him ' Brother ', he had once known as the
Great Hunters.

And to prove that this is a true legend, the stone of
Pa-ha-chi still closes the mouth of the cave in the White
Mountains ; and any one who looks upwards on a clear
night can see that Pa-ha-chi has set his star in the sky, as a sign
to mortals that he has entered the Happy Hunting Grounds.

THE WHITE HIND

THE Chief of the Birch Tree had three sons. The second-born, who was called Chi-oo, was discontented; for sometimes he wished he had been the first-born, who would succeed the Chief, and sometimes he longed to be the youngest, who he thought was his father's favourite.

The tribe had a legend concerning a valley, where there was said to be a small lake; and he who drank of its water thenceforward would be the acknowledged leader of all who saw him. Chi-oo decided that he would make the journey there, but when he told his companions where he was going they only mocked him.

' Chi-oo is a fool! ' they shouted. ' A fool who believes that legends are true. Poor Chi-oo! He will be chased by a grizzly, or fall off a rock and hurt himself, before he has gone a day's walk from the circle of tepees . . . and we shall have to look for him, and bring him home as though he were still a child! '

And every time they saw him they asked, ' Have you forgotten the Forgotten Lake, Chi-oo? ' or, ' Was your journey so short that you are back already? '

At last he grew so angry that he forgot the dignity necessary to his father's son and threw stones at them : which was cowardly, for, as he was the son of the Chief, they could not throw stones at him. So they ran away, stopping to jeer only when they had outdistanced him.

Then Chi-oo decided to hide in the forest for many days, and return only after he had invented a story of such extraordinary adventures that every one who heard it would be profoundly impressed. He stayed in a cave on the hillside for the span of a moon ; bored and lonely but too proud to return. He expected his companions to be awed by his story, for it contained a battle with three grizzlies, and the slaying of two enemy warriors. But one of his companions had followed his tracks, and they all knew he was lying : so when he finished his story and waited for their praise, he heard mockery louder than ever before.

So, hoping to prove that he was indeed a mighty warrior, he brought back two scalps : but even though his companions did not mock him, he took little pleasure in their praise ; for he knew that the scalps belonged to two youths who had been sitting talking under a tree, and that he had fallen upon them from above and killed them while they were still too startled to defend themselves.

Chi-oo always refused to join in the work of the tribe, for he thought it beneath his dignity : he would not even help to strip bark for making canoes, or look for flints that would be good arrow heads. He was proud of avoiding these commonplace tasks, and tried to believe that no one laughed at him for being lazy.

The Chief was growing old and a little credulous : so when the mockery became more than Chi-oo could bear, he spoke to his father of those who had most tormented him, and with great subtlety brought discredit on them. When suspicion had been thoroughly aroused and his father questioned him, he pretended to be very reluctant to say anything against his friends : which convinced the Chief that Chi-oo was warning him for the good of the tribe. So the Chief made sure that the men whom he suspected of treachery suffered; though instead of a more direct penalty (which would have required Chi-oo speaking openly before the Council of Elders, which he refused to do) they were either sent to spy in a hostile hunting-ground and fell into an ambush, or else were sent to skin a grizzly that instead of being dead was only slightly wounded.

The only person who never laughed at Chi-oo was the daughter of his mother's sister. He took very little notice of her, for he thought she was too young to be worthy of his attention, but when he sat by the camp-fire listening to the story-teller, he knew that she believed the legends, even as he used to do.

One day he found her making a pair of moccasins, 'They are for you,' she said, ' to wear when you make the journey to the Forgotten Lake.'

He laughed. ' There is no such lake. Though you are only a child, surely you don't believe such a silly story ! '

' I believe it : and so do you. I know that one day you will find it, and then all the people who have mocked you will be ashamed that they were so blind, and they will ask you to lead them.'

' And hate me, because I am wiser than they are ! '

' No,' said the girl, ' they will love you . . . and then you will be as wise as you want to be.'

Chi-oo tried to make himself believe that he was only sharing in a child's game. ' If I wear your moccasins will they show me which path to follow ? '

' Yes, and if you lose the way you have only to ask them to find it for you.' She traced the design with her finger. 'Look, I have put a white bead for each day's journey . . . and a blue bead to show you where you must think extra carefully.'

' What is the red bead for ? '

She smiled. 'That is the day you will come home : the day when you will begin to be happy.'

' I'm happy now,' he said defiantly.

' When they mock you ? '

' They only mock because they are afraid of me.'

' You can't be happy while people are afraid of you : that

is why you are going to make the journey. The moccasins will be finished to-morrow, and I will put them in your tepee, so that you need not tell any one when you are ready to go.'

Chi-oo had no intention of looking for the Forgotten Lake, but when he saw the moccasins he slipped his feet into them to see whether they were too large or too small. They were strangely comfortable ; in them he felt more free even than when running with bare feet on close turf. Suddenly he realized that he had always meant to find the lake : he would start to-morrow, without telling any one where he was going.

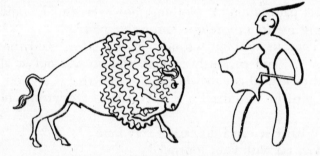

And when he returned they would all have to acknowledge him as their leader, and with his new authority he could mock them and they would not dare to run away !

It was dawn when he set forth, and it seemed that the moccasins chose the path, the path which led towards the rising sun. On the seventh day he came to an open plain, where a solitary black bison was tossing its head and pawing at the ground. The moment it saw Chi-oo it lowered its head and charged at him ; and he only escaped by climbing a tree which grew on the edge of the forest through which he had come.

As soon as he was hidden by the branches, the bison walked away and began to browse on the sparse herbage. But whenever Chi-oo tried to come down from the tree the bison heard him, and he only just had time to scramble out of its reach. Then as soon as it had watched him climb to the highest branch it trotted away and appeared to forget all about him.

Chi-oo hoped that after nightfall he would be able to escape, but the bison must have been able to see in the dark, for he heard the thud of its galloping hooves almost as soon as his feet touched the ground : it nearly caught him that time, for the lowest branch snapped when he tried to swing himself on to it, and he felt the bison's breath hot on his foot as he drew it up to safety.

By the evening of the second day he was getting very hungry, and the sound of cool water running over a nearby rock didn't make his thirst any easier to bear. He looked down at his moccasins, and said bitterly, ' You are not very good at path-finding ! Nothing, however stupid, could have brought me to a more uncomfortable place ! '

' There is nothing wrong with the *place*,' said the moccasins . . . and curiously enough Chi-oo was not at all surprised to hear them answer him. ' The tree is a good home for a bird or a squirrel ; it is you who are wrong, not the place.'

' What else can I do except stay here ? '

' Get on with your journey.'

' And be killed by the bison,' he said indignantly.

And a mocking-bird, who had alighted on the topmost branch, shrilled, ' Killed by the bison ! Killed by the bison ! Poor Chi-oo is frightened, frightened, frightened ! '

Chi-oo was so angry that he swung down from the tree and started to run across the plain. The bison, which looked larger and blacker than ever before, only missed him by a finger's breadth, and it stood under the tree, pawing the ground so furiously that the boughs quivered as though in a winter gale.

' Stupid ! ' said the moccasins. ' Very stupid ! '

' Well, what else could I have done ? ' said Chi-oo, who by now was not only indignant but thoroughly frightened. ' You told me not to stay up here, and now you call me stupid when I try to escape.'

' We could show you the way,' they said, in their small clear voices which fluted together like two reeds. ' We could show you the way, if you would ask us politely. We are very

insistent on politeness, aren't we?' they said; and before he could answer, they added, ' Of course we are!'

' Then *please* will you show me how to cross the plain without being killed by the bison?'

' Ask the White Hind,' they said, as though amazed that any one could have failed to think of such an obvious solution. Then, as they saw the bewilderment of his face, they added impatiently, ' Go on, call it!'

So Chi-oo shouted, ' White Hind! White Hind! Please come and help me!'

To his amazement he saw a white hind come trotting out from the shadow of the forest: her horns and her hooves were of silver, and her coat, which was without blemish, shone like water in the sun. He saw her trot fearlessly up to the black bison, who, instead of charging at her, showed every sign of delight at her appearance. She kept just ahead of him, pausing from time to time to make sure that he was following. Whenever she found a patch of succulent grass she stopped to graze and let him share it with her. Further and further she led him away, until they were a black speck and a white on the border of the plain.

' Hurry up!' said the moccasins; ' there is plenty of time for you to cross the plain before the bison remembers you, if you don't waste your opportunities.'

So Chi-oo climbed down from the tree and ran as fast as he could; until he was so tired that he had to walk. Then he walked, though very slowly by the end of the day, for it was a wide plain.

He started the next day's journey feeling comfortably full, for he had found a patch of corn and made a fire over which he roasted some of the ripe cobs. The country was open and rocky, with patches of sage brush. He was walking along, whistling and feeling proud of himself for having passed the bison, when the mocking-bird circled overhead and shrieked:

' Chi-oo is walking into danger! Chi-oo doesn't know that the ground here is only a thin crust over the Underworld. Chi-oo can't hear the demons, who are chuckling because they know he is going to fall through a hole into their food-basket.

The demons are wondering whether he would taste better boiled in coyote's milk or fried in his own fat!'

Chi-oo was so frightened that he scrambled up a rock and crouched there, covered with cold sweat although it was a hot day. The ground shimmered in a heat haze, and Chi-oo saw it was dotted with curious holes . . . holes that might have been made by people falling through to the demons.

There were holes even by the path along which he had come, so he dared not retrace his steps. Sometimes a thing peered at him from one of the holes, but it vanished before he could see what kind of faces these demons wore.

Three times he collected enough courage to crawl down from the rock and take a few hesitant steps, but the mocking-bird shrilled, 'Boiled or fried, Chi-oo? Boiled or fried?'

And he was so frightened that his legs wouldn't hold him upright and he had to crawl back to the rock on all fours.

It was evening before he thought of calling to the White

Hind. 'White Hind, help me!' he shouted; 'but be careful of the demons or they will catch you too.'

The White Hind came trotting towards him: and to his horror he saw her put her foot into one of the holes. She stood still holding up her forefoot as though she were lame. She was so beautiful that Chi-oo forgot his fear, and he ran towards her across the pitted ground. But before he reached her she vanished.

'Before you try to crawl back to your rock you had better look more closely at the holes,' said the moccasins severely.

Chi-oo, to his own surprise, did what he was told. And instead of looking down into the Underworld he found himself peering into the entrance of a gopher's house: and instead of demons, hundreds of gophers had come out of their holes to look at a man who was more timid even than themselves. He walked past them very quietly so they should not be disturbed: and they sat up on their haunches to watch him, and decided that they had never before seen anything so large and yet so harmless.

The next country he came to was well wooded, and he found plenty of berries to eat and pools of clear water. He felt very cheerful, so the mocking-bird had to scream louder than usual before he took any notice of it.

'Danger Chi-oo! Don't shelter in a cave when it begins to rain, for a rabbit lives there and it might attack you! Danger, Chi-oo! Don't go into the cave!'

Chi-oo pretended not to have heard the mocking-bird, and decided that should he happen to find a cave he would walk straight into it without hesitating, just to prove he was not afraid of anything ... especially of rabbits, however fierce. Early in the evening it began to rain, and when he saw the mouth of a cave loom up through the curtain of falling water he splashed towards it; delighted to think that in a moment he would be able to kindle a fire and warm himself.

The mocking-bird laughed to see how easily he had fallen into the trap it had prepared: for the cave was the home of a particularly disagreeable puma. She was gorged with a kill made earlier in the day, so when Chi-oo entered her cave she remained hidden in the shadows, knowing that she could kill him with a blow of her paw whenever she felt hungry.

Chi-oo lit his fire and sat beside it, whistling and feeling proud of himself. The puma watched him : she would have liked to purr, but refrained in case he heard her. Soon, Chi-oo curled up by the warm ashes of his fire and went to sleep. A little thread of saliva drooled out of the puma's mouth as she thought how delicious he would taste when she felt sufficiently hungry to do him justice.

Chi-oo dreamed that the White Hind came to the cave, stepped over his sleeping body . . . and that he watched it fight with the puma a terrible soundless battle. The flank of the White Hind was slashed open by the savage claws : then one of her silver horns pierced the puma's heart, and it fell back dead.

When Chi-oo woke he knew he could not have been dreaming, for on the floor of the cave there were the prints of beautiful hooves and drops of bright blood in the white sand. He made himself go into the shadows ; and there he found the dead puma, its lips curled back from the cruel teeth that to-morrow would have eaten him. And Chi-oo wept, that the White Hind had been wounded because his pride had let him be betrayed by the mocking-bird.

The next day he came to a wall of mountains : they were smooth and impossible to climb, but in one place they were cleft as though by the blow of a giant's tomahawk. Yet he could not pass through this cleft, for it was closed by five redwoods, which grew so close together that only a lizard could have crept between the mighty trunks. Yet through this narrow chink Chi-oo could see the lake, the forgotten lake, gleaming in the sun.

He spent many days trying to scale the cliffs, but the rock was so smooth that even his moccasins could not find a foothold. The redwoods had no branches low enough for him to reach, so he began to cut an opening through the trunk of the central one. But the bark was so tough that at the end of a day's work his flint knife had only carved a nick very little wider than the palm of his hand.

'But a nick is better than nothing,' said the moccasins consolingly. 'And if you work every day from dawn until sunset you will in several years make a hole large enough to crawl through.'

And the mocking-bird screamed, 'In a few years Chi-oo will be an old man . . . an old man when he returns to the tribe . . . old enough to be a story-teller instead of a warrior!'

But Chi-oo took no notice of it, and went on chipping away at the bark. When he woke next morning he found that the nick was twice as big as he had left it; and the same thing happened the next day and the next. So that night he stayed awake, to try to discover whom he should thank for helping him.

He heard a soft padding on the path from the river where he bathed every evening: twelve beavers came into sight, and began gnawing industriously at the trunk. He thanked them, very humbly, and the eldest beaver said:

'We watched you working, and our chief decided that as you had made such good progress, considering the inadequate teeth available to you, it was our duty to help you as a fellow-worker.'

When Chi-oo repeated his fervent thanks, the beaver said:

'Nothing extraordinary in it I assure you. The tree needs cutting through, and therefore it is our job to assist. The dam is the main thing, not the beaver who makes it.'

'I am not cutting the tree for a dam,' said Chi-oo, who regretted that his honesty compelled him to say this, for he thought it would stop the beavers helping him any more.

'Not for a dam? How extraordinary!' chorused the beavers; but the eldest of them said sharply, 'Be quiet, all of you! We have been told to be helpful, but the outcome of our help is no concern of ours.'

So the beavers, looking embarrassed, hurried back to their gnawing. Before dawn the hole was large enough for Chi-oo to crawl through; and the beavers stood watching him, bewildered that any one should leave a tree which would be so admirably suited to a dam, but resigned to the incomprehensible behaviour of non-beavers.

At last Chi-oo could see the lake, small and perfect in the circle of cliffs, more blue even than the sky at noonday. It was surrounded by reeds, which swayed in the gentle breeze and made a curious hissing noise.

' Careful, Chi-oo ! ' said the moccasins sharply, ' Look where you nearly put us ! '

Chi-oo looked down and saw that what he had taken for a dead twig was a viper. It was not the only viper, for the hissing sound was not wind in the reeds ; it was made by snakes, hundreds of snakes, as many as there are ripples on a wind-ruffled lake !

Chi-oo tried to run : but his feet wouldn't move.

' Stop ! ' shouted the moccasins. ' The snakes will get you if you run . . . you're only safe so long as you face them ! '

The snakes, who had been pouring over the ground towards him, suddenly coiled ; their heads slowly swaying from side to side as they watched him. The hissing became louder : it was no longer a formless sound, but broken up into words.

' He is a coward. No, don't kill him, he can be useful to the tribe ; let him make cooking-pots, for he is not worthy to be a warrior. He was frightened of the grizzly. He stole arrow-heads because he was too lazy to make his own. He lied : the deer he followed did not leave our hunting-ground, he lost its spoor. His spear did not break . . . he threw it away and fled. He said the Chief was growing old. He said that a younger man should lead us. He broke a branch from a birch tree without confessing to the totem.'

Suddenly Chi-oo realized why the words of the snakes were so terribly familiar : they were the same words he had used to his father to bring a subtle vengeance on his companions.

' You can't run away,' said the moccasins. ' Walk towards them : their poison cannot harm you for you share it with them.'

But Chi-oo had always been afraid of snakes, even those

which he knew to be harmless . . . and these snakes were more horrid even than rattlers. He realized that the moccasins were not going to let him run, not going to let him stay in the only patch of ground that was free of snakes : they picked up his right foot and made it take a pace forward . . . they were forcing him towards the snakes.

'You can't escape from the echoes of your own voice,' they said sternly.

He felt the snakes brush against him as though he were forcing his way through dry grasses. Their tongues flickered against his skin, and he felt it cringe with anticipation of their fangs. Step by step the moccasins dragged him forward.

'We were sent into an ambush,' hissed the snakes. 'You knew that the grizzly was not dead. . . . You knew that the canoe was too rotten to go down the rapids. . . .'

Chi-oo recognized the voices ; the voices of his companions who had died because he had betrayed them to his father. He was going to die, as they had died : but he could remember that he was a warrior of the Birch Tree.

'I am not afraid of you,' he said ; and found that what he claimed was true. 'I have betrayed you, but I am no longer a traitor. I was your enemy, but now I am your friend, for I am no longer a coward. When I enter the great hunting-ground to join your company you will no longer mock me : for Chi-oo, the man whom you despised, is dead. . . .'

He shut his eyes, waiting for a hundred fangs to drive their poison into his flesh. Nothing happened : he opened his eyes, and saw that the snakes had disappeared. Only the reeds rustling in the breeze broke the silence ; and on the path that led through them there was not even the track of a snake, yet in the white sand there were narrow hoof prints, the prints of beautiful silver hooves.

He ran forward, crying out, 'The White Hind! The White Hind!'

She was standing in the shallow water on the fringe of the lake, watching the path by which he came. But as he splashed towards her, she vanished. And Chi-oo wept, for he longed to be with her.

'Aren't you going to drink,' asked the moccasins, 'now that we have brought you all this way?'

But Chi-oo was thinking of the White Hind, and said absently, 'Drink? No, why should I when I'm not thirsty?'

'Don't you want power over people? That is why you came here, isn't it?'

'Did I?' said Chi-oo. 'I forget, but I think I came here because it is the home of the White Hind . . . and now she has vanished.'

'Won't power satisfy you? You always wanted power.'

'Would it help me to find her?'

'Not unless you share it with her; not unless you both drink the water at the same moment.'

'Then I will carry it with me until I find her,' said Chi-oo. He filled the water-skin he had carried during his journey, and as he did so a few drops of water splashed his eyes and washed the dust from them.

'Where shall I start looking for her?' he asked the moccasins.

'It was on the plain of the black bison that you first saw her, so perhaps the forest which borders it is her home.'

'Yes,' said Chi-oo, 'I will go back to the forest.'

When he reached the mountains which circled the lake, he found that the cleft of the five redwoods had disappeared. But on this side the mountains were not impossible to climb : slowly he pulled himself from ledge to ledge, sometimes with no better handhold than a crack wide enough to take two of his fingers.

It was evening before he reached the top : during his climb he had hoped that as the cleft had disappeared the cliffs had also changed and would no longer be quite sheer. Now he saw that because he had not a rope over a hundred paces long he must either remain a prisoner of the cliffs, or fall, to lie at their feet in a little heap of whitening bones.

'Don't worry,' said a warm and kindly voice, 'we will make a ladder for you, stronger than a rope and much easier to climb down.'

'Of course we will,' chimed in many other voices. And Chi-oo saw that snakes were pouring up the ledge towards him.

'Just wait until we arrange ourselves in sizes,' said the snake who had first spoken. 'Hook me over that spike of rock,' it said, the voice rather indistinct because it had its tail in its mouth.

Chi-oo did as he was told, and then watched in amazement as snake after snake looped itself through the one in front of it and then took its tail firmly in its mouth.

'Hurry up!' said the moccasins. 'Don't keep them waiting, for that position must be most inconvenient.'

So Chi-oo stepped on that warm and living ladder, and went down rung after rung, snake after snake.

They didn't even wait to be thanked, for the moment he was on firm ground they started to climb up themselves, and in an unnaturally short time they disappeared over the skyline.

Chi-oo was tired after such an exhausting day, so decided

to spend the night by the river. When he reached the bank he found the twelve beavers waiting for him. He asked them if they would mind his spending the night in their company, and explained that he was too tired to go any further until he had rested.

The eldest beaver stepped forward, coughed, ran its claws through its whiskers, and began a speech which had obviously been carefully rehearsed :

' We, the Beavers, greet you, the Non-beaver, having been ordered to do so by our Chief, an order with which we are all in full agreement. As a token of our respect and fellowship we have made a small portable dam, similar to those in which certain tribes of non-beavers are accustomed to travel. We should be honoured if you were to find it of use, and should you wish to sleep it would be our pleasure to escort you down-river as far as you wish to go, or up-river should that be the direction in which you prefer to proceed.'

Then the beaver pointed to where a small raft was moored to the bank. After expressing his gratitude, in the most formal terms he could think of at such short notice, Chi-oo gratefully lay down on the raft. The beavers, who sat on each side of him, paddled so vigorously with their tails, that even though they travelled against the current they made most excellent progress.

Feeling very refreshed after his soothing river journey, Chi-oo exchanged affectionate farewells with the beavers and by nightfall reached the puma's cave.

To prove to himself that he was no longer afraid, he decided to spend the night in it. As there had been heavy rain during the afternoon he could find no dry kindling with which to start a fire ; so he sat cross-legged in the mouth of the cave, listening to the rain dripping off the trees.

' Cold, isn't it ? ' said a small voice ; and he looked down to see a rabbit shivering inside its fur.

' Yes,' said Chi-oo, ' very cold. I am so sorry that I have been unable to build a fire by which you could have warmed yourself.'

' I don't want to *presume*,' said the rabbit, who appeared

to be overwhelmed with shyness, ' and I hardly like to make the offer . . . my help is sure to be so insignificant. . . . I hope you will not be annoyed. . . .'

' How could I be ? ' said Chi-oo, trying to put it at ease.

The rabbit pricked up its ears and looked a little more confident. ' Not so good as a fire, but better than nothing . . . or I hope that you may think so.'

' I am sure it would be,' said Chi-oo, who had no idea what it was talking about.

' Then you will allow me to lend you my coat ! Oh, I am so glad ! ' it exclaimed. And while he was trying to think of a suitable answer, it dashed off to the back of the cave. There was a scrabbling noise, as though it was trying to pull something heavy along the floor, so, thinking it might need his help, Chi-oo went to see what it was doing.

The rabbit was dragging a puma skin towards him : the pelt finely cured and supple. ' To keep you warm,' it said. ' *My* coat . . . but I can assure you that it holds no trace of the unpleasant me which used to occupy it.'

' *Our* coat,' said Chi-oo : and with a delighted squeak the rabbit jumped into his arms.

And that night the safe warmth of the puma skin wrapped them both close against the cold.

After helping the rabbit to fold up the fur robe, and promising to return to spend a few days in its cave as soon as he had the opportunity, Chi-oo again set forth on his homeward journey.

He had not gone far before he saw smoke rising in the distance. Knowing that this part of the country had not been allotted as a tribal hunting-ground he approached cautiously, to see whether the smoke came from the cooking-fires of a tribe on peaceful migration, or whether it came from an encampment of warriors who might be hostile to his own people.

They were Black Feathers : with them were neither children nor squaws . . . and from the direction of their trail it was obvious that they were contemplating a raid on the Birch Tree.

Chi-oo knew that even if he warned his tribe it would not

save many of his companions from death, for the Black
Feathers outnumbered them by more than three to one. The
enemy were encamped on a small rocky hill, which stood like
an island in a sea of sand and scrub.

'We will help you,' said an urgent whisper. And Chi-oo,
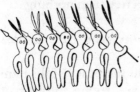
who had been wriggling across an
open patch of ground so as to get
closer to the enemy without being
seen, found himself staring into the
face of a gopher.

'Am I right in thinking that
you dislike these rude and barbarous people who have
invaded our territory ? ' it asked politely.

'Quite right,' said Chi-oo fervently ; 'I dislike them very
much indeed.'

'Then may I take it to be understood between us that you
would not be grieved if something should *happen* to them ? '

'If it were something unpleasant I should be delighted ! '

'Just as I thought ! ' said the gopher. 'I am always afraid
of being officious, but this seemed such a very clear case.'

Chi-oo couldn't imagine how such inoffensive animals as
the gophers could cause the Black Feathers any inconvenience,
and it must have realized his doubt for it said in a hurt voice,
'I do not wish to remind you of anything unpleasant, but you
may remember that when we last met you thought that under
here there was, shall we say, a large and empty space into which
it would be highly undesirable to fall.'

'Yes,' said Chi-oo uncomfortably, 'I am afraid I was so
stupid as to mistake you for demons.'

'A very natural mistake,' said the gopher, obviously
flattered. 'But there really are caves here, very deep caves
which hold an underground lake. When we first came here
some of the more energetic of us would insist on digging too
deep, and we had several nasty accidents, sudden and very
final. A long pause, and then a splash, and then nothing. It
made some of my relations so nervous that they moved away.
Ever since the arrival of these people, whom we so much
dislike, we have been digging through the floors of our

houses . . . or rather, I should have said, the floors of those houses which form a circle round the rock which they are occupying. There is now only a thin crust of sand remaining, and I can assure you that it would not bear the weight even of a very small man. You realize, of course, that I have arranged that the unsafe ground is too wide to jump . . . so they can choose whether to stay here for ever, or try to escape . . . when they will pause while they wait for the splash.'

Chi-oo was still not sure if the gopher was exaggerating, and, being a discerning animal, it said huffily, ' If you do not wish for our help I will instruct the others to repair the damage done to our houses ; damage which has caused us considerable inconvenience.'

' Please don't do that. . . . I am most grateful.'

' Well, then, prove it ! ' said the gopher sharply. ' And unless you do I shall order the repairs to begin at once. Jump up and give a war whoop . . . and see what happens when they try to catch you.'

Chi-oo reluctantly got to his feet and shouted the challenge of the Birch Tree. The encampment boiled like a cooking-pot, and the Black Feathers, brandishing their tomahawks, surged down the rock towards Chi-oo, who, though he found it exceedingly difficult to do, stood his ground.

There was a loud crack as the ground gave way under their feet : and where the leading file of warriors had been there was now a cleft beyond which huddled the terrified remnants of the enemy.

' I hope you will not again be so incredulous,' said the gopher. ' And in future do not judge the value of a friend by his size, nor mistake a fully justified caution for unpardonable timidity.'

When Chi-oo tried to express the profoundness of his gratitude, it said briskly, ' Yes, yes, but I've no time to listen to all that. Very kind of you, I'm sure, but I must go to see if there are any cracks in the foundations. Good-bye ! Good-bye ! And very pleased to see you any time you're passing.'

So, as it was no use making a speech of thanks to gophers who were too busy to listen, Chi-oo went on his journey.

When he came to the plain the grass rippled from horizon to horizon, but there was no sign of the black bison. In the distance Chi-oo could see the line of the forest where he thought to find the White Hind. He was so impatient to see her that he began to run without giving due attention to where he put his feet : a loose stone turned under his right foot and wrenched his ankle so badly that he could only limp forward very slowly.

'White Hind ! White Hind, wait for me !' he cried out, 'I am coming to you as fast as I can, but wait for me !'

In the distance he heard the thud of galloping hooves : but it was not the White Hind, it was the black bison, charging towards him across the plain. It was no use trying to run away, for he was lame, and there was no tree to climb . . . and as the White Hind had not answered him he felt it mattered very little if the black bison killed him : so he stood still.

The bison thrust out its forefeet, but it was galloping so fast that it was difficult for it to stop suddenly. It was snorting, not with anger but because it had galloped so fast that it was breathless.

'Sorry to keep . . . you waiting,' it said between gasps. 'Didn't expect you until this evening . . . or should have been ready sooner . . . sincere apologies . . . your ankle entirely my fault . . . discourteous of me to allow you to walk. . . .'

Then it spread out its legs so as to make it easier for Chi-oo to climb on its back.

'Tell me if my trot is a bit too bumpy,' it said politely, 'and please use my mane to hold on by if you find it of any assistance.'

When they entered the forest the mocking-bird screamed at him, 'Poor Chi-oo, the lame one ! No one wants a lame man to lead them !'

Chi-oo looked up at the mocking-bird and said gently, 'I am very sorry that you are so unhappy.'

'I am not unhappy,' said the mocking-bird indignantly, 'I laugh all day long !'

'You laugh *at* people, not *with* them, so you must be unhappy.'

A curious thing happened to the mocking-bird : it began to moult. Its feathers fell faster than dead leaves in a gale : then for a moment it was as naked as though it had been plucked for the cooking-pot. And new feathers began to sprout, the feathers of a wood-pigeon, which are the colour of the horizon.

The pigeon lighted on his shoulder and caressed his ear with her beak. 'I will never laugh at people again,' it whispered, 'for I shall share in their contentment.'

The bison trotted forward into the dappled shade of the forest. Standing beside a white birch tree was the Hind ; her silver hooves and her silver horns shining like water in the sun. Chi-oo leapt from the bison's back and ran towards her, his lameness forgotten. But before he reached her, she vanished, and in her stead a girl stood leaning against the birch tree : a girl even more beautiful than the hind. And Chi-oo knew that it was she with whom he would share the water of the Forgotten Lake, for it was because of her that he had made the journey.

They kissed each other, and together they drank the water : then hand in hand they went back to the tribe, to lead them into happiness.

And if you ask Chi-oo why his wife has a scar on her right shoulder, he will tell you that it was made by the claws of a puma who fought with a White Hind.

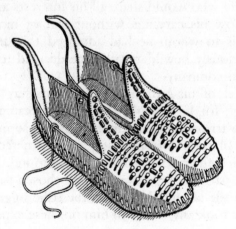

THE HEART OF THE BIRCH TREE

ROKINI was a warrior: because his ancestors, for more generations than could be counted on both hands, had always been warriors. He would have much preferred to be a wood-carver, but, in the opinion of the Elders, this was an occupation suitable only to the crippled.

He had not taken a squaw, for in that tribe women were considered of little importance: they lived apart with the small children, weaving blankets and cooking the food. He wanted a wife who would share all his interests and to whom he could show his carvings without fear of mockery; but the two girls to whom he had admitted this ambition had been so obviously bewildered that he decided to be content with his own company.

The Chief of his tribe never let them stay long in the same locality, for he thought that if life became too easy it might turn warriors into husbandmen; so as soon as they had cleared the place-of-corn-growing and garnered one good harvest, he led them to a new hunting-ground. As Rokini was the best path-finder he was usually chosen to explore the land beyond the boundaries before the tribe migrated.

He never took any one with him on these expeditions, for

he enjoyed being alone; and by his solitary camp-fire he could carve birds and animals instead of using his skill on the shafts of arrows. One day he came to a small lake, beside which grew a single birch tree that afforded the only patch of shade. It was noon in the hot weather, so he sat under the tree, whistling.

Suddenly he realized that some one was singing to his tune: a woman's voice, clear as falling water. The shores of the lake were empty, so he knew that the singer must be hidden in the branches above him. He stared up through the leaves, but seeing no trace of any one he called out:

' Woman with the beautiful voice, come down and talk to me.'

' I *am* down,' said the voice sadly. He thought she must be teasing him, for the tree trunk was too narrow to conceal even the most slender woman.

' Shall I climb up to you ? '

' You can climb me, but not *to* me,' said the voice.

He took hold of the trunk and shook it until the leaves rustled. ' Come down, or I shall shake the tree until you fall.'

' You won't make me fall, but you may make me a little giddy . . . the spring gales often do.' Then she added hastily, ' Don't be too rough or you might break one of my branches, and that is always rather uncomfortable. I lost a branch a few years ago, but the wound is healed and I don't think you can even see the scar.'

' If you don't stop teasing me I shall shake much harder . . . but don't be frightened, for I shall be here to catch you.'

Rokini thought it would be very pleasant if she fell into his arms, for he was convinced that she would be as beautiful as her voice.

' Oh, *don't* be so silly,' she said pleadingly; ' I am *not* a woman . . . at least not an ordinary woman.'

' Of course you're not . . . that's why I am so impatient to see you.'

' But you *can* see me ! '

' No, I can't. Not even your smallest toe or a strand of your hair.'

'You are standing on my smallest toe, and my hair is hanging all round you.' Then, seeing that Rokini was getting still more bewildered, she said, 'Can't you understand that though I think like a woman I look like a birch tree ? The root you are standing on is my smallest toe . . . no, you needn't get off, for it doesn't hurt me ; and my hair has turned into leaves . . . though of course in winter it is only twigs.'

Rokini was startled, but not incredulous as a more ordinary warrior might have been, though to make quite sure there was not a woman hidden in the branches he pinched the trunk between his finger and thumb ; and the voice said, 'Don't do that . . . . it tickles ! '

So he sat down and put his arms round the smooth, white trunk and leant his forehead against it, and said, 'Though I grieve, my beautiful one, that you are a birch tree, at least you will never be alone any more : for I shall stay here until I die, and then my bones shall be buried under your roots.'

'You would find it very dull here after a few years,' she answered sadly. 'I didn't mind for the first half-century, but it grows very monotonous, year after year.'

'Not nearly so monotonous as living without you. I have been so many journeys and had so many adventures that I have plenty to tell you about . . . which should make it a little less dull than you were without me.'

'Much less,' she said, and a sigh whispered through the leaves. 'But after a while you will want a woman who can travel with you. No, it's no use pretending. . . . I know you don't want the kind of woman who is content to wait for your return : you want one who can share everything with you. . . . I know very well, for I used to be like that.'

'The woman for whom I have always longed ! '

'Yes, I know ; but that only makes things even more difficult for us now. I wasn't content to stay with the squaws ; I wouldn't accept any man who expected me to sit at home and make blankets ! But I was the only daughter of a chief, and he wanted me to have a son who could succeed him. He offered me the choice of all the young braves, but I thought each was as dull and slow-witted as the rest . . . they could talk of nothing except hunting, and expected me to praise their extraordinary stupidity ! '

' What happened then ? ' said Rokini anxiously.

The leaves stirred despondently. ' Oh, the usual thing : my father ordered me to be put to death for disobedience, and one of the old squaws—she had had three husbands and hated them all, so she sympathized with me—said that she could save me by magic. She turned me into a birch tree, and meant to turn me back again as soon as Father stopped being so disagreeable : but she had mislaid the other half of the spell, so I have been like this ever since. There was some talk of making me the totem of the tribe, but I think Father found it embarrassing to have me watching him, so after a time they migrated. I don't know where they went, but they took the path to the West.'

' How could they leave you ! ' exclaimed Rokini indignantly. ' Surely even a man who was blind and deaf would still know that one of your leaves was worth all other women ! '

' I am so happy that I want to dance ! Oh dear, how very tiresome it is to be rooted ! '

Suddenly all her branches quivered with excitement. ' I have remembered something very important ! We needn't stay here, for I can come with you ! '

' You have remembered the spell ? '

' No,' she said regretfully, ' it is not so exciting as that . . . but I needn't live in *all* the tree, only in part of it.'

' How do you know ? '

' A hunter once made an arrow out of one of my branches ; it was a small one so I didn't miss it . . . and I found myself in his quiver ! Luckily I realized in time what a dull man he was, so I managed to get back here before he had gone very far. Another time a man carved a string of beads out of me as a present for his wife. I went home with him to see what she was like, but they quarrelled so much that for a time I was quite content to be a birch tree.'

' What shall I carve for you to live in, my beautiful one ? '

' It must be small enough for you to carry, but not too small or you might lose me.'

'I shall never lose you. Are you sure it won't hurt when I have to cut through your bark?'

'No, it will be a lovely feeling . . . but hurry, for I long to share adventures with you.'

So from a branch of the white birch Rokini carved a heart. '*Our* heart,' he said to her; 'a single heart which will share all things.'

On the top he made a little hole so that he could wear it round his neck on a rawhide thong.

'Now I am warm and alive,' she said, 'and the snow or the winter winds don't matter any more, for I am safe with you.'

'Where shall we go?' he asked. 'Do you want to visit my tribe, or shall we look for an adventure?'

She sounded surprised. 'We must look for a squaw who is good at magic, so that she can tell us the other half of the spell.'

'You said it happened more than a hundred years ago. . . .'

'Yes, I know: but magical squaws always tell their secrets to their daughters, and she had three, one by each husband. I hope the children didn't take after their fathers, for the first was half-witted, the second blind, and the third had such a violent temper that even the braves were afraid of him.'

'Then why did she marry them?'

'Because no one else wanted her: she was small and wizened, but her magic was stronger than her husbands were, and none of them lived more than a year or two.'

'You are sure that your tribe moved westwards when they deserted you?'

'Yes; but it is not among them we must look. Each daughter married into a different tribe: the eldest into the Grey Smoke, the next into the Hornet, and the third . . . well I don't really know what happened to her, for she was carried off in a raid by the Black Feathers; so we hoped that she died.'

Rokini well understood her feelings, for the Black Feathers are feared and hated by all other tribes.

'The Grey Smokes are friendly, and their hunting-

grounds adjoin ours to the north-east, so we had better go
there first. We can listen to their story-teller, which should
be the quickest way to find out how much magic they know.'

In five days they reached the Grey Smoke. This tribe
never migrated, for they had found that the plant from which
they took their name and for whose cultivation they were
famous, preferred to be grown in the same ground year after
year. The Chief was glad to see Rokini, for he had promised
to give five bundles of the leaf to the neighbouring tribe, in
exchange for cooking-pots, and Rokini's arrival would save
him the trouble of sending them by one of his own people.

As he was so friendly, Rokini decided it could do no
harm to ask him whether any of his tribe were skilled in magic.

'Nearly all of them,' said the Chief proudly. At which
Rokini was delighted, for surely among so many there must
be at least one who knew the second half of so ordinary a spell.

'Have you any one who could turn a birch tree into a
woman?'

The Chief laughed. ' We can do better than that ! We can turn seeds which look insignificant as a smear of dust into a winter of contentment. And who would not say that even one night of contentment is worth more than all the women on Earth ? '

' But if a man preferred a certain woman. . . .'

' Then I should say that he had never savoured good smoke. My people value the Plant-of-peace far above squaws, for though they have to work hard during the time of the growing they know that instead of dreading the winter, as other men do, they will pass it in a cloud of enjoyment. And their delight can be kindled at their wish, instead of depending on the contrariness of women : and the smoke brings men closer in friendship, unlike women who often divide them against each other ! '

' Is the smoke the *only* magic you can do ? '

' It is more than that,' said the Chief emphatically; ' it is the only magic worth doing ! '

So Rokini left the circle of tepees, carrying with him the five bundles of leaves : but as he had no intention of going home he hid them in a cave until such time as he would be free to fetch them.

' I am afraid it has been a very disappointing day,' he said despondently, but she answered :

' No it hasn't ; for I learned a lot of interesting things.'

' About smoke ? '

' Much more useful. I used to think that if I found a man who wanted to work with me I should be quite happy, but now I know that isn't enough. The men and women of the Smoke work together, but they don't think about each other. Plants are the only things which matter to them. While the Chief was showing you his fields I listened to the people talking. Do you remember the two who had just been betrothed ? '

Rokini nodded, and she went on, ' I thought he was telling her how beautiful she was . . . actually she was rather plain, but he oughtn't to have thought so. What he really said was, " I found two caterpillars on a leaf this morning ",

and she looked as horrified as though he had said he didn't
love her! Then I noticed a mother crooning to her baby,
but instead of whispering fond nonsense she was saying,
" When you have opened your second pair of leaves you will
be ready for transplanting ". There was a man very angry
with his wife : she cringed as though he had cursed her really
effectively, but the words he used were, " The sight of you
reminds me of a spot of mildew on the new crop ". Even as a
birch tree I could still dream of happy things I would do as a
woman ; but these people haven't even dreams . . . they are
less intelligent than plants ! '

When they reached the Hornet they found the Chief
busily directing the construction of a stone wall round the
encampment. He paused only long enough to greet Rokini,
and then said anxiously :

' Sorry I can't stop to talk. We are expecting an attack
at any moment. Black Feathers have been seen by two of
our trackers, and though I am doing everything possible I
expect most of us will be dead before nightfall.'

The squaws were scurrying about ; putting bundles of
arrows at vantage points along the wall and preparing cauld-
rons of pitch for the staunching of wounds. Realizing that
it was not an opportune moment to mention magic, Rokini
accepted the suggestion that he should help to build the wall.
He expected an attack before dawn, but when, after three
days, nothing happened, he wondered why the frenzied pre-
parations showed no sign of abating.

He was tired after carrying so many heavy stones, and had
sat down to rest for a few moments when a woman came up
to him and said sharply, ' If you have nothing to do, make
something. Don't you know it is a sin to be idle ? ' Then she
hurried off before he had time to answer.

He was wondering how soon he could leave without it
appearing as though he were running away, when the heart
said to him :

' Now I have discovered something else I needn't believe
in. I thought that if men had to be warriors, women had
better be warriors too : but look what has happened to these

people ! They have killed so many enemies that they think they are bound to be attacked. They are not really expecting the Black Feathers . . . this is the way they always behave between raids.'

' How do you know ? '

' By looking at the women. They wear the same clothes as the men ; no decoration, not even a few beads on their moccasins ! That's why they are all scurrying about, trying to hide from their terrible boredom ! '

' Do you think there's a hope that one of them knows a little magic ? '

' None. For if they did they would use it to stop themselves being so miserable.'

To which Rokini had to agree ; so feeling very depressed he left the Hornet . . . who were so busy that they never noticed his departure.

The two were so engrossed in their heart that Rokini missed the signs which should have shown so experienced a tracker that he was approaching the Black Feathers. Before he had time either to hide or to run away he was surrounded by warriors who refused to believe that he came in peace. They bound his wrists and ankles with raw-hide thongs which bit into his flesh, and then drove him along the path in front of them, shouting with laughter whenever he stumbled.

Their Chief also took it for granted that he was an enemy, so they left him at the foot of their totem pole while they decided which of their special tortures would provide them with the greatest amusement.

' Hide me behind one of the carvings,' she said urgently. ' I may be able to help you from there : if they see me round your neck they are sure to steal me.'

Although he was helpless as a trussed wild duck, he managed to gnaw through the thong which held the heart, and with his bound hands thrust it into a crevice of the totem. Then he lay still, wishing that his courage was not so small a flame to light the darkness of his fear. He knew that the Black Feathers were as proud of their tortures as more friendly tribes are proud of their canoes, and to bring slow death

after the maximum of pain was the height of their ambition. So when he saw the warriors, led by their Chief, approaching him, Rokini shut his eyes, trying to gather up every small grain of courage with which to face them.

Then from the totem came a loud and commanding voice : a voice beloved of Rokini, but which to the others was heard as the symbol of dark authority.

' In the name of the Lord of the Black Feathers, hear me ! This man, whom you have laid at my feet as a sacrifice, should have been welcomed with the homage due to my envoy ! Strip the feathered head-dress from your chief, and give it to the new-comer whom I have appointed. Obey, or feel my wrath ! '

A man in the leading file stretched out his hand to pull the head-dress from the chief. For a moment he hesitated : and the clouds which had obscured the sky since early afternoon were riven with lightning, and thunder drummed across the plain.

To them this was the final proof : flinging themselves prostrate, they wriggled forward, their foreheads pressed to the ground in token of abject submission.

' How lucky that they are not better at foreseeing the weather,' she said contentedly. ' I *always* thought the Black Feathers were very stupid ! '

Rokini had to wait to receive the homage of his enemies ; then, after they had conducted him to the chief's tepee and brought many gifts to propitiate him, he announced that he wished to be alone, and that every man and woman of the tribe was to spend the night closed in their tepees while they asked the totem to forgive the disgraceful reception of his envoy.

When all was quiet, Rokini left the encampment, still wearing the head-dress in case any one who had disobeyed his orders might observe his stealthy departure. After going what he judged to be a safe distance, he kindled a fire in which to burn the head-dress and after the last feather had been consumed, he scattered the ashes in running water . . . which is an effective way of destroying objects of evil.

7

As neither of them could think of a new direction in which to continue their search for the spell, Rokini thought he had better go back to his own Chief, who by now would be impatient for news of the lands beyond their present boundaries. The evening of his return he went down to the river, and there found a squaw sitting on the bank with her fourteen children. He recognized her as the only woman who was supposed to be entirely content, and he had often heard envious remarks made about her by the other squaws.

While he watched, the baby began to scream because it was hungry; a little girl, about a year old, howled because she had fallen and hurt her knee; two of the older boys started to fight; and another one hit his head while trying to dive and was nearly drowned before his mother rescued him. While she was holding him head downwards to shake the water out of his lungs, two girls began to pull each other's hair, so fiercely that they seemed in danger of losing their scalps.

Rokini was so sorry for the poor woman that he went up to offer his help. The sight of a warrior taking any notice of their mother so impressed the children that they stood still, staring at him and forgetting to be tiresome.

'What a beautiful silence!' exclaimed the woman, sitting down abruptly as though her legs were too tired to carry her a moment longer than was necessary. She sighed, 'How I wish there was something I could do to show my gratitude!'

With sudden hope Rokini said, 'Do you happen to know any magic? For instance, a spell which could turn a birch tree into a woman?'

The woman paused, and then said, 'Spell? Yes, I have got one, though I never tried it myself. It came down to me from my great-grandmother, who was carried off by the Black Feathers but escaped to our tribe. I don't know where I put it . . . it was written on a piece of doe-skin. . . .'

Then she smiled. 'How silly of me! I've got it here; I always carry anything of value with me to keep it away from the children.'

She put her hand down the neck of her tunic and drew
out a small leather bag ; from it she poured out her treasure
on the flat rock beside her.   Five carved wooden beads, a

piece of beeswax, a broken bow-string . . . and a little roll of
doe-skin.

' Here it is,' she said.   ' You can have it if you like, though
it has never been any use to me.'

She watched him take the down-river path, and sighed ;
knowing that as soon as he was out of sight the children would
break into clamour.

' Did you hear, my heart ?   Did you hear ? ' said Rokini,
his voice trembling with excitement.   ' In a moment you will
be a woman again.'

' Is all the spell there . . . both parts of it ? '

Hastily he scanned the faint writing-signs. ' Yes, it is all here.'

' Rokini, would you mind very much if you only used the first part of it . . . on *yourself* ? '

' The *first* part ? But . . . '

' Yes, I know. But you would be very happy as a birch tree. Men and women always seem to work, or fight, or quarrel . . . and they grow old so soon.'

' Happy lovers never really grow old.'

' But they have such a lot of children . . . and if we were both the *same* birch tree.'

' Yes,' said Rokini slowly. ' If we were both the *same* birch tree. . . .'

On the shores of the small lake the white birch is no longer solitary : round it spreads a forest. For Rokini and his love are so very happy together.

HOPI THE HUNTER

HOPI was a hunter, so famous that he was spoken of in awe beside the camp-fires of seven tribes. His Chief sometimes wished that Hopi was not quite so remarkable, for he provided the fish and meat, furs and skins, needed by the whole tribe, so the other braves seldom bothered to kill anything larger than a mosquito : it was possible that his prowess provided sufficient honour for the other men's flabby muscles and slothful habits to be overlooked, but of this the Chief was doubtful, knowing that a forest cannot be made from one tree.

The tribe carefully concealed the manner of Hopi's death, for it was unfortunate that so mighty a man should die through swallowing a blow-fly. Hopi knew what had killed him, but being aware that the Great Hunters do not allow a single failure to blind them to a multitude of virtues, he was confident that after his body had received the correct funerary ceremonies they would welcome him to the Happy Hunting Grounds.

He lay in the death canoe, thinking of the celestial quarry which he would soon be following in noble company :

fact, he was thinking of this so hard that he was entirely oblivious to the praise that was being chanted in his honour by a thousand warriors—which was a pity, for the chants would have added to the self-confidence of which he was soon to find himself in need.

He felt the death canoe caught by the current which swept it towards the rapids above the whirlpool : then it was sucked down into the dark vortex of water . . . to glide smoothly on, as it entered the river which runs through the Land beyond the Sunset.

The canoe reached the bank, and Hopi stepped out on a platform of white stone. It was deserted, which surprised him, as he thought that the arrival of so famous a hunter would already have been known. In front of him was a high doorway, its pillars carved like a totem, in the face of the cliff. As it obviously led to the home of some one of importance, Hopi decided to go there to bring the welcome news of his arrival.

He had always thought of the Great Hunters as being like men, wearing the head-dresses of mighty chiefs : men, though Hopi had the modesty not to mention it to any one, who would most probably closely resemble himself. Inside the great doorway he found a room as large as a cavern ; and here were assembled many presences. Hopi did not find this at all surprising, for it was reasonable to suppose that the Gods met in council in the manner of tribal elders . . . though of course bringing wider knowledge to their decisions and more illuminating results. But he was startled to see that although the seated figures had the bodies of men they had the heads of animals.

As he entered, the presence on his right, which he took to be their spokesman, said to him :

' Hopi the Hunter, you have obeyed our summons to come before us : and it is our judgement which will decide whether you can enter the Happy Hunting Grounds, or must return to Earth in such form as we may find suitable. Our decision will rest on the answers you can give in truth to the questions which my companions wish to put to you.'

Hopi felt a little embarrassed, for as a hunter he had never

expected to meet the Lords of the Animals, whom he now realized these august presences undoubtedly were; so he answered, in a voice considerably less arrogant than was usual to him:

'I pledge my word as a warrior that my mouth shall utter no falsehood.'

Then spoke the Lord of the Red Deer: 'I have been informed that during your lifetime you have killed five hundred and seventy-three of my people. What was your motive?'

'So that my tribe should not go hungry,' said Hopi.

'Did you leave any one of them to die of wounds because you were too lazy to follow its tracks and set it free of pain?'

'No,' said Hopi; 'a hunter of my stature never wounds an animal without expiating his clumsiness with the gift of a swift and painless death.'

'Then I have no quarrel with you,' said the Lord of the Red Deer.

Then spoke the Lord of the Bears, saying, 'How many of my people have you killed?'

Hopi answered, 'Eighty-three, of which, and this I deeply regret, four were cubs.'

'And what was your motive?'

'With twelve it was because they had become old and savage, and were a danger to any of my people who might cross their path. The rest I killed because their fat is much esteemed by my tribe: it has, as you know, a number of uses, from curing a stubborn cough to rendering moccasins impervious to damp.'

'And the cubs?'

'In each case I had killed their mother before realizing that she had a young family. I thought it better to kill them than to leave them to starve.'

'Your carelessness was inexcusable, but as you have at least had the honesty not to try to conceal your fault, I hereby declare that I have no quarrel with you.'

Then spoke the Lord of the Wild Geese, saying, 'How many of my people have you killed?'

'Twenty-seven : but all when they were in flight.'

'What was your motive : think well before you answer ? '

It was difficult to admit to a fault before all those watching eyes, but Hopi said, ' Because I was the only person with sufficient skill to send an arrow through the neck when they were flying. It was said to be impossible, but I proved this to be false. The flesh of the birds was greatly appreciated by my chief, who after first tasting it was always urging me to repeat my performance.'

' This story I find most disagreeable,' said the Lord of the Wild Geese, ' composed as it is of pride and gluttony. But as it seems unlikely that any one will be able to follow your disgraceful example I am prepared to say, though with some reluctance, that I too have no quarrel with you.'

Then spoke the Lord of the Bison, saying, ' How many of my people have you killed ? '

' Five : though in full honesty I must admit that there might have been more had your herds been prevalent in that part of the country in which I lived.'

' And your motive ? '

' To provide food for the tribe, who were at that time migrating across the plains, and to secure hides with which to make a tent worthy of the chief . . . your hide being praised above all others both for its beauty and durability.'

'A very fair answer,' said the Lord of the Bison : and Hopi hoped that he was right in thinking that there was a note of genuine warmth in the voice. He was beginning to feel much more confident, for surely as he had passed the tests given to him by the four most formidable figures he had very little to fear.

Then spoke the Lord of the Trout, saying, ' How many of my people have you killed ? '

' I am afraid I don't know,' said Hopi, ' for among our people a hunter does not keep a tally of fish, except they be salmon.'

' And what motive had you for killing these uncounted numbers ? '

' Food,' said Hopi firmly. ' I can assure you that trout are highly prized by us.'

' You have lied ! Many trout have you killed to use for food, and for these I have no quarrel with you. But you killed many others of which you had no need : you left their bodies to rot on the river bank, or to starve in fish-traps you were too idle to attend. You killed us for amusement, or in an attempt to demonstrate that you were more clever than your companions . . . who must have been excessively stupid for such an idea to be held even by one so credulous as yourself. So there *is* a quarrel between us, and how it shall be decided I will state only after hearing what you have to say to the two of us whom you have not yet answered.'

Then spoke the Lord of the Otters, saying, ' How many of my people have you killed ? '

It was with considerable discomfort that Hopi had to say, ' Six hundred and thirty-nine.'

' And what was your motive ? '

Thinking that perhaps one lie might pass unnoticed, Hopi said loudly, ' To collect sufficient of your most valuable pelts to make moccasins for my people : as you well know, there is no pelt so eagerly sought for this purpose.'

' You have lied ! ' said the Lord of the Otters. ' It is possible that in your later years you indeed killed us because you required our fur : but this would not account for a quarter of the total number. As a boy you killed otters because they were large enough to satisfy your vanity, yet not sufficiently fierce to be really dangerous. Your success engendered in you a lust for killing, and because you knew your father would disapprove of this senseless slaughter you buried the bodies of your victims or left them to rot. You did not even refrain from this disgusting sport during the breeding season, and many a family of infant otters have starved to death because your cruelty prevented the return of their mother. I find you extraordinarily disagreeable, and it is with pity for Earth that I send you back there ! '

Before Hopi could think of any way of pleading with the Lord of Otters for clemency, the Lord of the Cougars spoke to him, saying, ' How many of my people have you killed ? '

Trying to gulp down his disappointment, which was nearly as difficult as he had once found the fatal blow-fly, he answered :

' Thirty-seven.'

By now he was eager for any lie with which he might hope to defend himself, so when the Lord of Cougars asked, ' And your motive ? ' he answered without hesitation :

' Because during the cold weather I wanted every squaw to have the comfort of a fur robe in which to sleep. Such robes are so highly valued that they are passed down from mother to daughter, sometimes for three or four generations.'

He hoped that this would flatter the Lord of Cougars sufficiently for him not to inquire into details : he was disappointed.

' You have lied ! It is known that you were glad to bring back to the tribe a trophy so highly prized as is one of our pelts, but you were not in the least concerned whether the squaws slept warm, or whether their teeth rattled with cold like pebbles shaken in a cooking-pot. You have killed us, not because our presence brought your people into danger, for in fact our hunting-ground and their's were widely separated : you tracked us without mercy, because we were known to be skilled in defence, and so killing us brought you the praise you so avidly desired—and which you so little merited. It is with profound apologies to Earth that I send you back there : and I can only hope that you may encounter some one of your own measure—there is no punishment more horrible that I can contemplate ! '

Then the Lords of the Animals spoke together, saying :

' Hereby we give judgement that Hopi is not worthy to enter the Happy Hunting Grounds. In clemency we cannot order him to become each thing he has killed, for that would

occupy too long a span of time : instead he shall become all that has killed him.'

Thereat, to his extreme discomfiture, Hopi found himself contained in the body of a blow-fly : a blow-fly that was sitting on a small mound of dung which the tribal outcast had failed to remove when cleaning the encampment.

He knew, though he had been scornful of such things while in the body of a man, that one of the old squaws was reputed to have some small skill in magic . . . perhaps she would be able to restore him to human shape : it was at least worth trying to attract her attention.

She was asleep ; so he tried to wake her by crawling along her nose and when this had no effect he stamped across her forehead. She woke angry at being disturbed : and instead of taking any notice of his frantic buzzing she nearly squashed him before he flew sadly away.

He tried twice more during the afternoon, but all that happened was that she crippled one of his legs before he escaped. He decided that humans were as dangerous to blow-flies as blow-flies, on occasion, could be to humans : so he flew down to the river and alighted on the body of a dead toad which appeared to offer a safe and convenient raft.

A trout rose to the surface ; but he was too abstracted to notice it. It snapped, and ate him. . . .

And Hopi found himself in the body of a trout.

He was determined not to kill anything in case such action should bring unpleasant consequences, so he swam about, nibbling water-weed which left him increasingly hungry. The other fish kept away from him, for as they saw he was not eating properly they thought he had an illness which might be catching.

He spent many lonely months, and one day he was floating gloomily in the shadow of the bank when an otter saw him, and dived. There was a scrunch. . . .

And Hopi found himself in the body of an otter.

He was determined not to eat any fish, although his belly kept on reminding him of its delicious flavour until saliva

dripped out of his hungry mouth. He knew the way home
to the hole where the otter had lived with his wife; but she
recognized that there was something odd about him and only
snarled when he tried to speak to her. So he huddled under
a tree and moped; and the other otters pretended not to see
him.

It was nearly two years later that he saw the cougar
crouching to spring: but he was so depressed that he couldn't
be bothered to run away. The cougar played with him before
she made the kill, which was very uncomfortable. Then
there was a gulp. . . .

And Hopi found himself in the body of a cougar.

It was quite agreeable being a cougar, for he was a young
one who hadn't taken a mate, so there was no one to despise
him for being different. He lived alone in a cave, and had
plenty of time to think long and disagreeable thoughts about
the circumstances which had brought him there. He first
felt angry with his father and mother, who had encouraged
him to be a hunter instead of training him to do something
which had less dangerous consequences, such as building
canoes or making arrow-heads. Then he decided that perhaps
it wasn't their fault and that the blame lay with the chief, who
had driven him to excessive killings so as to bring fame to the
tribe. He became more and more convinced that it was most
unfair that the chief should not share in the trouble he had
caused, especially as he was no doubt still basking in the fame
of Hopi the mighty hunter; Hopi in whose praise a thousand
warriors had chanted.

So Hopi the cougar decided to stalk the chief until he
found a suitable occasion in which to tear him into a large
number of pieces. But the cougar was so intent on the kill
that he fell into a pit, on some sharp spikes that had been put
there for just such a probability.

The tribe was short of meat at the time, so they cut him
up and put him in the cooking-pot. A little girl (she was an
orphan and so ugly that she never got enough to eat unless
she grabbed it for herself) saw that no one was watching the
stew so she crept up and pulled out a lump of cougar-meat.

And Hopi found he was a little girl, who was crying because she had burnt her mouth.

He was so relieved to be human again, even though it was only as a female child, that he was very careful never to be annoying to anything. To be on the safe side he lived entirely on vegetables, and never picked one without asking its permission and then expressing thanks for its courtesy. He visited all the fish-traps three times a day, to release any fish that had strayed into them; and so as to warn otters and cougars, and any other animals who might be in the neighbourhood, he used to follow the hunters, making as much noise as possible.

Needless to say the hunters took a hearty dislike to this child who, however often they ordered her to go home, always reappeared at the most inconvenient moments. They seriously considered asking the chief to declare her outcast, but decided that if this became known they might be mocked by the hunters of other tribes.

In time Hopi grew into a squaw, and one day was following three hunters who were on the track of a grizzly. She intended to start singing or clapping her hands as soon as they got close to it, but she never carried out the plan as an overhanging cliff collapsed, killing all four of them.

The hunters knew that when death in unforeseen circumstances makes it impossible for the proper funerary ceremonies to be carried out, the Great Hunters are willing to dispense with such formalities. They were waiting to be summoned to the Happy Hunting Grounds, when to their extreme disgust they realized that the squaw had followed them even to the Land beyond the Sunset.

Their horror increased when she strode confidently ahead, beckoning them to follow her. She led them to the platform of white stone, and across it to the doorway in the face of the cliff.

As they passed between the carved pillars they saw her change into Hopi: Hopi the Hunter whose praises they had so often chanted by their camp-fires.

Then they heard the Lord of the Heron, who is the spokesman of the Council, say to him :

'In our names we welcome you in honour to the Happy Hunting Grounds : where animals, and men, and Gods, find peace in company.'

THE CAVERN OF THE BLIND FISH

A WOMAN of the tribe of the Blue Jay had twin sons, who were so alike that when asleep not even their mother could tell them apart; but when they were awake no one could mistake them, for Dakis was clear-sighted as a falcon, and Dakoo was blind.

The boys were so close to each other that sometimes it seemed as though they shared their sight, for as Dakoo grew older he learned to recognize all the different birds by their songs, and could tell one tree from another by the sound of the wind in their leaves : the dry patter of the silver poplar, the majestic creak of a lone pine, the slow soughing of a redwood.

Every day, at sunset and sunrise, Dakis asked the Great Hunters that he might restore sight to his brother ; and when he was fifteen an old man, wearing no tribal mark on his forehead, came to the Place of the Blue Jay and asked for shelter.

The tribe were suspicious of strangers, but they offered him food and a night's rest, which is the least that must be given to strangers who come in peace. After he had eaten with the others in the circle of firelight, the old man asked that he might be allowed to tell them a story, in gratitude for what he had received.

It was a story which did not belong to the legends known to the Blue Jay, and told of a country to the south, where there was a cave through which a man could enter the Underworld. Few there were who had ever made the journey, for it was very perilous ; and the caverns were so vast that they were known as the Country-under-the-Earth. Of the brave men who had entered them very few had ever returned, and they seemed to have lost their memory or else were too frightened to speak of what they had seen. In sleep they muttered of clouds of demons that had swooped down on them from the darkness, of monsters whose slimy trails glistened on the dank floors of caves that stretched to infinity : and their voices rose to a scream when they spoke of the Cavern of the Blind Fish.

The tribal story-teller resented the stranger, and was obviously delighted when no one took any interest in the tale. When the old man paused, the others pretended to think he had finished and drifted away, leaving him alone with Dakis.

' Please tell me more about the Cavern of the Blind Fish,' said the boy eagerly.

The old man smiled. ' You think I know more ? '

' I am sure you do. Why are they blind ? Why are men terrified of them ? '

' Why do you want to know ? '

' Because to me it might be very important. My brother is blind. . . .' And he told him about Dakoo, and how he prayed every day to the Great Hunters that one day he might restore his sight.

' Now I know why I came here,' said the old man. ' I knew there was some one to whom I had to tell this story : had I been wiser I should have recognized you, and so not had to weary the rest of your tribe with my conversation.'

Dakis put another log on the fire, for it was a cold night, and then sat back on his heels to listen.

' The people of long ago would not have considered youɪ brother especially afflicted, for to them all this tribe would have seemed blind.'

' I am afraid I don't understand,' said Dakis apologetically.

'Neither would they : but it is still true. The "forgotten people" could see the shape of the song of an oriole, and to them the Lord of the Redwood was as clear as the face of a friend. They did not have to address their prayers to a totem, for the Great Hunters were as elder brothers with whom they walked in company.'

'Why can't we see them ? '

'Because men grew jealous of the Gods, and refused to listen to their counsel. They pretended they could not see them : and one day they woke to find it true.'

'What happened to their eyes which could see the Gods ? '

'They are hidden in the Cave of the Blind Fish. Every one has two pairs of eyes, Dakis : the ones he uses for ordinary things, and those which make him aware of the spirit.'

'Could the other eyes see ordinary things too . . . things like birds and trees, and where the rocks are when you steer a canoe down a rapid ? '

'Nothing is hidden from those eyes.'

'If I found mine could I give them away ? '

'You could ; though no one has ever wanted to part with so great a treasure.'

'But if they were mine I could do what I liked with them, couldn't I ? '

'Yes, if you found them. But have you forgotten that in living memory no one who has returned from those caverns has dared to speak of what he saw there ? Most of them pretend to be dumb ; yet in sleep they scream in terror.'

'Will you tell me how to find the caverns ? '

'Yes,' said the old man, 'I will tell you the way.' And picking up a stick he began to draw a map in the ashes. Hills and mountains ; a river that Dakis must follow until he came to a plain that he must cross. Then more hills which led to rolling grassland. And he gave Dakis detailed instructions how to find the entrance cave, which looked quite ordinary from the outside and was hidden by a thicket of brambles and young willows. Then he drew another map, of the stars ; so that Dakis could find his way if he journeyed after nightfall.

In the morning the old man had gone : Dakis never knew that he waited in the forest to watch him start on his quest.

Dakis found it very difficult to say good-bye to his brother : they had never before been parted, and he knew how lonely Dakoo would be without him. He could not tell him where he was going, for he knew that Dakoo was resigned to blindness, and that if he hoped for sight and was disappointed it would make things so much harder for him. So he had to say that he was going away to prove his courage as a warrior, and with this Dakoo was content ; it being quite usual for boys to be alone while they prepared for the ordeals which they must undergo before they could wear the scarlet feather in their forehead-thong.

The old moon had waned and the new one was nearly at the full before Dakis reached the grasslands. He heard something fluttering in a thicket, and found a fledgling hawk but could not see the nest from which it must have fallen. He picked it up, and it clung to his finger, then settled down between his hands. He was afraid to leave it, for it might have been killed by a snake or a stoat before it was old enough to defend itself, so he took it with him. In three days it could fly, but after circling round it always came back to perch on his shoulder. As he was lonely, Dakis used to talk to the hawk, telling it about Dakoo, and how the eyes he needed were guarded by the blind fish.

One day he was crossing a dried-up river-bed when he

saw, growing among the stones, a single stalk of corn. The
ground was so parched that the plant was stunted and its
leaves had withered before the only cob was ripe. Dakis
was so sorry for it that he picked the cob and put it into
the leather pouch which he carried slung over his shoulder ;
intending to sow the corn in the first fertile soil he found, so
that the children of the little plant should have a happier
place in which to grow.

When he realized that he was getting very close to the

cave, he was so eager to
prove his courage that he
walked all night under the
full moon ; the hawk clinging to the shoulderpiece of
his tunic and occasionally
stroking his ear with its beak
to show him it was awake.

If the old man had not
drawn such a clear map and
given most exact instruc-
tions, Dakis would not have
noticed the cave : it looked
so very ordinary, and the
mouth was hidden by a tangle
of brambles and wild grape.
It was noon when he found
it, and as he had been travelling all night he decided to
sleep in the sun before looking for a suitable pine-knot
from which to make the torch he would need. He had
sufficient food with him to last several days, for on his journey
he had found all that he required and so still had the pemmican
he had brought from home. By nightfall he had finished
making the torch, and was looking for a sheltered place in
which to sleep until dawn, when he realized that as night and
day would be equally dark in the caverns he had no excuse to
postpone the ordeal.

Looking up at the sky he said to the Great Hunters,
' Please let me forget that I am only fifteen and not very brave.

Let me keep on thinking what it must be like to be blind, so that somewhere I shall find the courage to help my brother.'

The hawk rose up, spiralling higher and higher into the clear air; then poised; its wings burnished by the last rays of the setting sun. It plunged down like a stone falling through water: and as Dakis entered the cave he felt its claws cool against his shoulder, and its beak very comforting against his ear.

There was nothing unusual about the outer cave, which looked as though it might have been the home of a mountain-bear: but Dakis knew that one of the boulders at the back of it was loose and that when he rolled it aside he would see the opening into a narrow tunnel.

The tunnel sloped steeply down, and the roof was so low that he had to crawl, but when it sloped still more steeply it was wide enough for him to turn round and clamber down feet first . . . which was not easy to do while carrying a torch. Suddenly he found emptiness beneath his groping feet, and clinging with one hand to the rock he held the torch above his head and peered down. Below him the rock wall fell sheer to a floor of what looked like white sand. It was a long drop, more than four times his height. Hoping that the ground was soft enough to break his fall, and telling the hawk either to use its wings or to take a firmer grip on his tunic, he let go of his handhold.

He landed with a thud which jerked the torch out of his hand, but he could see it still smouldering a little way ahead of him. Getting slowly to his feet he stumbled towards it and blew it into flame.

The sand was very deep, and with every step he sank in up to his knees. It was only then that he noticed the heavy stench with which the air was sodden: it was not sand through which he struggled forward, but the decaying drift of centuries.

The torch showed giant shadows which menaced him from every direction. The rocks were twisted into shapes of horror, like the dreams of men who have been under torture. He whirled the torch round his head and the flame streamed out like a pennant : he saw, far above him, the black roof poised like the wings of the Lord of Demons.

The roof was getting lower : the blackness was no longer solid and immovable. It was breaking up into a thousand shapes of terror, swooping down on him with shrill, unearthly cries. His feet were clogged in the ancient decay of the floor, and the torch flickered as the cold sweat of horror crawled over his body.

'I can never escape from here,' despair said to him. 'I can never climb up the cliff. The demons have trapped me here, alone in the dark !'

He felt a sharp pain : the hawk had sensed his panic and bitten his ear to remind him that he wasn't alone. Then the hawk launched itself against the black shapes which were fluttering closer and closer to Dakis. Inspired by its courage, he whirled the torch to give more light for the battle with the dark enemy. The hawk released from its talons one of the dark shapes which fell at his feet : it was sufficiently horrible, but not a demon ; it was a giant bat.

Dakis was startled by the sound of his own laughter. 'It is only a bat,' he said aloud. 'Thousands of bats, but they are not dangerous to men.'

The hawk was still attacking, and the bats were trying to escape, cringing back into the shadows of the roof, where they hung in their hundred thousands.

Beyond the cave of the bats, the rock wall was split by a narrow cleft, so deep that when Dakis threw down a pebble echo after echo bubbled up to him. On one side of the cleft there was a ledge on which he could gain a precarious foothold. Slowly he edged himself along : one hand holding the torch, the other spread against the rock seeking for any small projection that would help him to keep his balance.

The hawk, which had returned to his shoulder, seemed to be asleep, but twice it gently pulled his hair when he had looked down into the plunging depths and felt giddiness break over him like a wave. He cut his hand several times on the sharp rock, and it was slippery with blood before the ledge widened into a flight of natural steps which led down

to the bank of an underground river. The water was black, smooth yet uneasy like pitch about to boil. It ran dark and silent, without a ripple.

Dakis walked forward, and stumbled over something which projected through the sand. He thought it was a stone; then he saw it was a skull, whitened by the centuries. The bank of the dark river was strewn with skulls: some so old that they had nearly fallen into dust, others to which the hair still clung . . . in one of these a warrior's broken feather was still held by the forehead-thong.

The old man had told him that it was beyond the river that he would find the eyes. He waded into the dark water: and jumped back only just in time to escape the clashing jaws of one of the blind fish. It shone with the cold light of decay and was tall as a man. Instead of scales it was covered with thick white skin, and the curve of the head was broken only by the fanged mouth; for it had no eyes.

When it realized that he had escaped, it sank out of sight; the dark water slid past as though the surface had never been disturbed. He made three more attempts to cross the river, but the fish attacked him with such ferocity that he sat down on the bank to consider what he had better do next. He was hungry, so he chewed a piece of pemmican; it was dry and tasteless but quite satisfying.

Suddenly he thought, 'I wonder if the fish are hungry? Is that why they attack: not through hatred but because they need something to eat?' He had often fed trout in the river at home . . . they ate grain. . . . 'I wonder what these fish eat?'

He remembered the corn he had rescued from the dry river-bed . . . he had forgotten to plant it and it was still in his food-pouch. If the fish liked it they might let him pass: at least it would show them that he was not an enemy.

He scattered a handful of corn on the water. Three fish swirled up to snap at it with desperate eagerness. 'I have got to cross now, before they remember me,' said Dakis loudly.

The water was very cold, but even in the middle of the

river he could still stand. The hawk climbed from his shoulder to the top of his head, for it objected to getting its feet wet.

As Dakis climbed up the far bank he saw in the distance a small light. He thought it must be a reflection from his torch, but as he drew nearer he saw it was coming through an opening in the rock. He hurried forward, thinking that there must be a hole in the roof of another cavern through which the sun was shining.

The light streaming through a low archway was so intense that it made him blink. For a moment he was dazzled; then he saw that the walls of the new cave seemed made of ice, for they glittered with sparks like splinters of a rainbow. Two natural pillars supported the roof. And between them stood the old man.

Dakis was curiously unsurprised to see him: it was almost as though he had known who would be waiting for him.

' You have done well,' the old man said. ' You are the only one who has crossed the river of the fish for more than five thousand years.'

' Then you will give me my eyes?'

' They are already yours . . . ' and into Dakis's hands he put two small round stones: they were the rich blue of the noon sky and seemed to hold within them a source of light. ' Now you can see me as I am.'

Dakis looked up: between the pillars there was no longer an old man; but a being, who wore the head-dress of a chief, feathers that glowed with white and yellow and scarlet. Then he knew that he was in the presence of one of the Great Hunters: yet instead of awe, he felt a warmth and a peace and a belonging, such as he had never experienced even in a dream.

And the Great Hunter spoke to Dakis, telling him many things: that the Hawk was born of his Will, and the Corn of his Kindliness, these being the two secrets a man must know if he may pass in safety through the Underworld.

When the time came for Dakis to return to his own people,

he found that there was no longer a dark river in the Cavern of the Blind : instead, a broad stream of clear water ran over smooth pebbles where little scarlet fish flickered among the water plants. The banks were of moss, studded with small blue and white flowers : and beyond them were stone steps, white as clouds on a calm day.

The Cave of the Bats was flooded with light ; and where the demon shapes had clung, the air was murmurous with doves and wood pigeons and other gentle birds ; and the floor of the cave was clean and firm as river sand.

The hawk flew ahead to wait for him at the foot of the steep rock which guarded the entrance cave. It seemed to grow larger, until its wings were wide enough to carry them both. Dakis was never quite sure whether he had climbed the rock, or whether the hawk flew with him on its back.

During the homeward journey he saw many things which before had been hidden from him. The blue and yellow pattern which a wren and a bullfinch make when they sing together : the brave shape of the colour red, and the quiet undulations of green. And when he reached the forest, the Lords of the Trees walked with him. They showed him the Dance of the Silver Poplar, and at night the pines welcomed him to the processional of the stars, and the incense cedars told him stories of the morning of the world.

He longed to travel very slowly, so that his new vision might give him many memories by which to live : but every day he walked from sunrise to sunset so that Dakoo should not have long to wait for his sight.

When he came to the hillside above the encampment, he gave the hoot of the snowy owl, three times repeated, which was the signal the brothers had always used between each other. He watched Dakoo running up the path towards him, for the boy had trained himself to know all the nearby paths until he could run almost as though he were not blind. He stumbled over a branch that had fallen since he last used the path : he hesitated, and cried out, ' Is it you, Dakis ? Is it really you ? '

Again Dakis gave the call of the owl ; and saw joy radiant on his brother's face.

Round Dakis stood the Lords of the Trees : the birch and the hickory ; the hornbeam and the alder ; the chestnut and the red oak ; the maple and the ash. 'In a moment Dakoo will be able to see them,' thought Dakis, ' but I . . . I shall only know that they are with me.'

Then he embraced his brother and said to him, ' Hold out your hands : for I have brought you a gift.'

The blue stones were cupped in the hands of the blind boy : then they vanished and he cried out, ' My eyes, Dakis, my eyes ! I can see you ! '

' Who else can you see ? Look, the Great Hunters and the Lords of the Trees have come to rejoice with you ! '

' It isn't pretence,' said the boy. ' I can *see* the trees, and now I know what " green " really looks like. A pine is taller than I expected, but the birches are just the same. That bird is " red ", isn't it, Dakis ? I only knew it as a singing shape until now . . . a brave shape like an arrow.'

' But can't you see the . . . others ? '

' I can see everything . . . you, and the forest, and the flight of a bird, and the lovely majesty of clouds. How can life be long enough to see all such beauty ? '

Then the brothers walked together along the path : and the Great Hunters smiled as they watched them go.

PRINTED BY
MORRISON AND GIBB LTD.
LONDON AND EDINBURGH